the unwanted wife

Secrets and Lies Exposed
An Arranged Marriage Hell

To Maggie
your Radiance is amazing
Thank you
SMaeck xoxo

SANDY MAECK

Disclaimer

The Unwanted Wife shares the writer's first-hand experiences and a lifetime of observation, discussions, research study and education, coupled with the experiences of other victims. Although some facts, references to cultural, customs and traditions may be based on actual events, names and events have been deliberately left out or changed for either legal, moral and privacy reasons.

It is the right of every victim to identify themselves when and if they choose to do so, and their courage should be respected.

Unless otherwise indicated, all the names, characters, businesses, places, events, and incidents in this book are either the product of the author's imagination or used in a fictitious manner. Any resemblance to actual persons, living or dead, or actual events is purely coincidental.

Testimonials

Thomas Maeck, Husband

"I am very proud of my wife Sandy for finally writing this book she sought to write for so many years. It took a lot of courage and bravery to make this essential step in her life. Sandy is strong, bold, and courageous. She has a heart of gold and is an amazing, loving and caring wife, mother, sister, daughter, and friend. I wish her nothing but success in her journey as an author. She has my love and support always.

Shevaun Ramdin, Daughter

To my amazing Mamadukes: Words cannot describe how proud of you I am; you have always been such an amazing and strong woman. You taught me how to be independent and never depend on anyone but yourself, and you set an excellent example for me. I am very proud that you've finally decided to take this step to write about this dark and disturbing topic. It takes a strong woman to do just that, and no one can take this away from you. You deserve every bit of it. Not only were you my mother, but you were also my father — some might not agree with that, but that's my truth. Growing up, you were my rock. You did whatever it took to give us what we needed, and you sacrificed your own happiness so many times for us, and I want you to know how much I appreciate that. It wasn't always easy, but you never let us see that... and being older now, I've come to realize how much you really did for us, and I love you so much for that. You are the best mother anyone could ask for, and I cherish you always.

Kevin Shah, Son

Everyone experiences life differently. However, not everyone understands hardship. Growing up, I watched you endured hardship, and no matter what, you prevailed — against whatever came your way. I'm proud of you for bringing awareness to domestic violence and abuse in our community and I'm so proud to call you, my mom. You're stronger than anyone else I've ever met. I can't wait for the world to see how far you've come. Don't ever give up.

I love you always!

Nirmala Ramsahoye, Sister

Sandy Maeck is my older sister, and I admire her tenacity and perseverance. She has always been a free spirit who was never afraid to go after the things she wanted. Growing up in a strict household, she was not afraid to break the rules and deal with the punishment later. She's always had a mind of her own and never allowed anything or anyone to bring her down. Thence, she was able to survive domestic violence and abuse. I am blessed to call her my sister and am very proud that she has the courage to tell this story through "The Unwanted Wife" and bring awareness to domestic violence and abuse for women like her who are ashamed or too afraid to speak for themselves.

Devica Yassen, Sister

I am proud of my sister on this extremely important achievement of completion of this book. Despite of all the hardships, she persisted, endured; never quit; kept going; stayed the course and now she has prevailed. Good job. I'm indeed proud of you for this wonderful achievement.

Richard Aziz, TV Host and Radio Personality

Sandy Maeck takes readers on a dark and twisted journey into the perilous world of domestic violence and abuse. There are so many horror stories on this subject that led to suicide and even murder. The Unwanted Wife is a must read for many women who are too afraid to speak out!

Reema Agarwal, Sr PIO, Nuclear Refurbishment

I have known Sandy (Shobha) Maeck in a variety of capacities for the last several years. She is my daughter's dance instructor and has trained and groomed her to grow into a fine young lady. She is an amazing role model for all her students for many years. Now that she has begun the journey of becoming an author, her venture into writing will influence lots of young women venturing into a world full of challenges and unpredictability. I wish her all the best.

Mintranie Captain, CEO Nexbizz Global Solutions

This story begins in Guyana and ends in Canada. Shocking truths are told, and horrible lies exposed. See how Maya's journey through domestic violence and abuse, led her to be the strong leader she became. Never before told from the point of view of a strong West Indian Woman, The Unwanted Wife is going to shock and intrigue many in our community. It is a must read!

Patricia Patoir, Friend, Confidante and Hair Stylist

I have known Sandy for over twenty years. She is a cherished friend and an amazing mother who would do anything for her children. She has raised them single-handedly, to be respectful and outstanding individuals. As her hairstylist and long-time friend, I have heard her stories – the good, the bad and the awful. I think this is the perfect timing for her book, since she has finally found love and happiness in Thomas. I wish her only the best in her endeavor as an author and coach.

Marlyn Haripersad, Friend and Confidante

Wow! A glimpse into the shocking journey of one woman's struggle and courageous efforts to escape her unfortunate situation and build a better life for her family!

Donna Phagoo, Parent, STCC Dance Academy

My girls are students at Sandy's Dance School, and it has been a remarkably positive experience for them. It has built their confidence and made them more open and sociable. Sandy has been an inspiration to them, to keep wanting to move forward. As the saying goes, 'behind every dancer who believes in themselves is a teacher who believed in them first'. Thank you, Sandy, for being an amazing role model for my daughters.

Ultimate World Publishing
Diamond Creek,
Victoria Australia 3089
www.writeabook.com.au

Dedication

**This book is dedicated to my beautiful children
and my loving husband**

To my children... This story tells that the strength of a mother is like no other. Just like Maya, I have given you my best. Know that you are the greatest thing that happened to me. During times of hardship and destitution, it was you that kept me going. It is you who continued to give me the strength to survive. I often struggled to find my way because I was facing my own personal demons, but your welfare and wellbeing always came first. I was not perfect, and I made many mistakes as a mother, but I never doubted my love for you, as it burns deeply in my heart always and forever. My love will always be with you, forever and always.

- Your loving Mom

To my husband... You have given me so much to live for. Your love, respect, and honor are something I didn't have until you walked into my life and changed it for the best with unsurpassed happiness. You have brightened my days and showed me that it is never too late to find true love. Thank you for pushing me to go further, encouraging me to write this book, and being my biggest supporter. Thank you for love and support you continuously give to my children. You are the kindest, most generous person I have ever met, and I am so thankful to have you in my life. I love you always, my soulmate.

- Your "Real Thing"

Contents

Chapter One

Fool's Curse

Whether you believe Maya's story is not important. Most of the time, she barely believes it herself. What is important are the lessons that it teaches. Paramount lessons, like trust, are necessary for love to survive, and great love demands an equal measure of sacrifice. Sometimes we do not realize this until it is too late. However, we are getting ahead of ourselves. This is Maya's story.

Maya grew up being told daily that she was the most beautiful girl in the village. People would compare her with Bollywood movie stars, the likes of Hema Malini, Rekha, Mumtaz. As she grew older, the offers for marriage started pouring in. She always refused. She was afraid. Afraid that she would make the wrong choice, that someone would find out her secret and she would be doomed forever.

Maya does not remember exactly how old she was when it started, but she was old enough to remember. Whenever they were together, she would catch Khalil gazing at her with looks that frightened and confused her. As often as he could, he would find some excuse to be alone with her. Khalil, her mother's younger brother, spent most of his summer holidays at their house in the village.

She remembers very clearly the first time it happened. It was summertime, Maya and her younger sister, Nadia, were spending summer holidays with their grandparents. Her grandparents owned and operated a pharmacy, and Maya was told to stay with her uncle at the shop until her sister and grandmother returned from the market. She does not recall where everyone else was at the time.

It started innocently enough. Khalil pulled her in playfully and told her to sit on his lap, offering her candy. Maya took it, opened the wrapper to plopped it into her mouth. He started to caress her arms, then her legs, then one hand was on her chest where her small tender breasts were now beginning to develop. The other hand went up to her dress to her panties. He touched her in places she knew he was not supposed to. Yet she sat there, terrified to move, letting him do this horrible, awful thing to her. The candy fell to the floor. Maya was in shock as this went on for what seemed like hours while she just sat there, frozen — horrified by what was happening.

Maya was only saved when a customer would come into the store. She was, however, not always this lucky. This horrible nightmare went on for many years, every chance Khalil got to be alone with her. Not until he left for Trinidad to attend university did it finally stop.

By then, she was almost fifteen years old.

Whenever Khalil returned for the summer, he would sit and stare at her hungrily. She tried to avoid him as much as she could and vowed that she would never let him touch her again. She started only wearing pants so that no one could ever put their hands up her dress again.

One summer, when Maya was about sixteen years old, Khalil once again returned home from school. It was a dreaded summer for Maya, and she always tried to stay with her cousins in the backyard while he was around. One day, as she was hurrying through the yard with a basket of flowers for her mother's morning *"puja,"* he grabbed her by the wrist. She looked at him in disgust, defying him to touch her, her body consumed with anger and hate.

"Our little Maya is turning into a natural beauty," he whispered in her ear.

"Please, uncle, mommy is waiting for me," she said, trying to pull away.

"Don't be in such a hurry, I just want a little closer look, for old time's sake," he loomed over her, his breath reeking of beer and cigarettes. "You're like a ripe mango, waiting to be plucked."

Maya managed to twist away, afraid of him, fearful of making a scene, fearful of humiliating her mother. But he was stronger than she was. He grabbed her arm and swung her around.

"Just one taste of your lips, little cherry," he leered.

"Maya, hurry up, mom is waiting," the high-pitched voice came from her sister, Nadia. She wondered to this day if Nadia saw and tried to save her. He let her arm go and chuckled as he inhaled the cigarette, his beady eyes gleaming in the hot morning sun.

Maya's cheeks were burning, she followed Nadia inside.

How could she explain to her mother, Premika, what was going on, what her own brother was doing — what kind of brother he was?

She will never believe me, Maya thought. Her brother was everything to her, he was her pride and joy. Khalil was handsome, intelligent, and treated Premika with so much love and respect. He had many girlfriends and was extremely popular. *Why would he interfere with me?* Maya could not understand what he wanted with her. She was young and barely had any breasts. Besides, she even looked younger than she really was. She could have easily passed for 12-years-old. He could have gotten any girl he wanted.

Why me? Maya continued to wonder in dismay. She used to study herself in the mirror as if looking at a stranger. She could not take credit for the long black hair, the fair skin, the oval-shaped face, and the dark lashed-over light gray eyes. These were a blessing from her ancestors. But what was the use of it to her if it was so impure? She was supposed to come to the man she marries pure and innocent. Not touched by evil hands, not tampered with. How would Premika believe that Maya did nothing to encourage him? She knew that her mother would be hurt. Maya had no wish to cause her any pain. If her father found out, he would surely kill Khalil, and her mother would be crushed. She could not do this to her. Maya felt broken.

By then, she was sixteen and not sure if she was a virgin. She knew it never hurt, nor did he penetrate her with his horrible fingers. Yet, she was warned so many times by her mother and "Nanie" of the horrendous consequences should anything like this happen. She heard rumors of girls losing their virginity by falling. She was terrified.

Arranged

Maya never saw her father have a loving exchange with his brothers or his sisters. He grew up believing that a father's only role was to provide financially for his family. She knew her family's history. She knew they loved each other. They were an exceptionally close-knit clan, but they did not show affection. Her paternal grandfather was a cowherd and supplied milk to most of the surrounding area at the time. He also owned most of the land that spanned two streets and a fabric store, in Kitty, Guyana, on South America's eastern coast. Her grandfather had built a reputation for his family as a staunch Hindu family dedicated to each other. A family that was dependable, loyal, and inseparable. They were the most respected and reputable family in the village.

This history made Maya realize that her father was a by-product of his upbringing: he was simply incapable of showing affection. Although he was not affectionate, her father, like his brothers, made his family the center of his life. Maya's father is the third son amongst five brothers and five sisters. None of his sisters finished school. They were trained to be housewives at an incredibly young age. Her dad and his two younger brothers were the first to finish school and work outside the home, but they still had to help in the evenings to clean the cowpen and mind the gardens. His two older brothers had to tend to the cows and the family's fabric store business.

Maya's parents met as arranged by her mother's aunty, just as her dad was about to embark on his career as a public health inspector. Her mother had just completed high school at one of Georgetown's most prestigious all girls' schools. Bali, Maya's father, was twenty-one and Premika was seventeen at the time. They even had the same birthday! Her father was very clever and a fast learner, and eventually followed in his father-in-law's footsteps to become the Chief Public Health Inspector in Guyana. Her mother was from a middle-class family who was highly educated in the medical and legal fields. After their marriage was arranged and they got engaged, they immediately set for Premika's older sister to marry Bali's older brother. It was a double wedding and the talk of the town for months to come.

Maya's grandfather died soon after Nadia was born. Maya was two years old at the time and does not remember her grandfather. Her father, his four brothers, their wives, and their children all lived in the same house. Each family had its own rooms, and the wives had their own kitchens. Maya was only a few months old when her parents decided that they wanted to live independently. After much debate, her father was given a small house and a piece of land in the backyard.

Maya's parents started from scratch, her father working for the government and her mother working fourteen-hour days running sewing classes through her dressmaking business. They eventually rebuilt the tiny house into one of the village's largest and most admired homes. By then, Bali was the Chief Public Health Prosecutor for Guyana. As the Indian community progressed, several outbreaks of political and race-based violence got worse. The country was getting more uneasy with political upheavals happening everywhere. Over the past two decades, there has been an unprecedented mass emigration of people out of Guyana to North America.

Deteriorating economic and political uproars caused emigration to increase even more sharply in the 1980s. Many of these emigrants were middle-class professionals, like her father, who opposed government policies. Being the public prosecutor for the courts and an immense follower of the PPP opposition party, her father knew that it was inevitable that he would have to migrate his family sooner rather than later. It was reasonable to want to leave and start a new life in Canada or America at the time. Everyone was trying their best to get the children married and to "go away."

By then, her parents had five daughters. Amid political upheaval and contentious riots, businesses and homes owned by Indian families were being hit by discriminatory racial acts. One such riot happened in the middle of a hot sweltering day. Armed soldiers arrived at their homes with guns and military gear. They sent her mother's customers and students away and pulled a truck up to the back of the shop. They left the shelves of her dressmaking business empty, which was devastating for her parents. Disturbed by the prospect of significant violence, her parents, like many others who most likely would face prosecution or worst, either for race, religion, or their past political activities, Premika and Bali decided it was time they left their homeland and venture to North America. They started from scratch once, they could do it again.

For this reason, they agreed to get their daughters married to families that lived away. When Maya's father arranged her marriage to the son of his old friend who lived in Canada, she was so scared, terrified that they would find out what had happened to her. She was supposed to marry young — there was no questioning that. In the Hindu religion, and following her family's traditional values, marriage was the only way a woman could honor her family. You either make a good wife, or you do not. You either produced healthy sons, or you did not. It was a woman's duty. Everything in their lives depended on this role. But Maya did not want any part of it.

At the age of seventeen, she had done very well in school and had graduated way before she was supposed to. Maya had already started college and didn't want to marry, she wanted to finish school and become a teacher at the college she was attending. She was offered the job even before graduating.

But Maya knew it was no use, she had to follow family tradition. Yet, she was feeling so defeated.

Like her sisters and cousins before her, Maya was born into her destiny, subject to her father, then her husband, and when he was dead, to her sons. She was born a Hindu woman, the privilege to be born as one. She had no right to wish for anything more. And yet, she dreamt of a young hero, like in the Bollywood movies, who would whisk her away from this humdrum life. She closed her eyes and conjured up his image, an athletic body, curly dark hair, eyes sparkling with humor, a man who could also laugh at himself. But her daydreaming was cut short.

It was announced earlier in the month that she was supposed to marry the younger son of Bali's friend, Sal. He was to arrive two nights before the wedding. She swallowed the lump in her throat when her mother told her it was Jason. She had learned early in life to hide her feelings and appear composed when she wanted to scream and stomp her feet. She kept her face blank. She did not want them to see her foolish disappointment. She always knew that her husband would be chosen for her, especially for migrating reasons. Maya remembered Jason when they were younger. She and her sisters used to play with him when her parents went to their house for visits. She always felt he was "girlish."

"Come on Maya, he is all grown up now. His girlish attitudes are all gone," her father encouraged. "He is a nice young man and living in Canada is going to be good for you."

Maya's parents consulted with the pandit, and her marriage was arranged for the spring of the following year. She slipped into the routine of an engaged young woman and waited for her wedding. She would not meet her husband-to-be until a week before the wedding. But then Jason's father called to say they were moving the wedding forward to the fall.

The preparations began immediately, as were the discussions about dowry, Indian bridal, and western bridal trousseau. It looked like it would take forever.

Premika was eyeing Maya suspiciously, "Whatever is the matter with you, Maya? Don't tell me this comes as a surprise to you?"

"No," she looked down at the floor. "Jason is the logical choice."

Logical! Premika thought. It was just like Maya to use such words to speak of her soon-to-be husband.

She got up from her chair. Premika is an immensely proud woman and was always immaculately dressed, her house always in order, and her children the best dressed in this part of the country.

She had five beautiful daughters, and she was proud of them. Maya was, however, the prized one. The fairest skinned, with long, flowing hair and beautiful eyes, she was the most beautiful. If her sisters were jealous, they never let on. Maya's older sister, Daya, used to comb her hair and always wished for long straight hair like Maya's, unlike her curly hair, which she chose to keep short.

As her mother got up, she called to the maid, "Come, we had better do something with her hair, I expect they will be here soon, and bring the green and gold dress."

Maya hated the green and gold dress. It was scratchy lace. She hated dresses and would have preferred to wear her comfortable jeans and t-shirt, but her mother would have been horrified had she even suggested this. Maya sat obediently as Daya offered to comb her hair. She always brushed it until it looked like black silk.

As she sat there, she wondered, *did her mother really expect her to be happy with Jason?* True, young brides were supposed to be happy with their assigned husbands. Her mother's marriage was arranged, and so were her older sisters.

They seemed genuinely happy with their husbands, even though they had little time for their wives. Still, she knew this was not the overwhelming passion like in the Bollywood movies. The passion people call "love." Maya didn't want logic; it was love she craved.

Within two months, it was wedding time. The hustle and bustle and the excitement of the upcoming wedding of a typical Guyanese Indian house was in full swing. Bags of rice, dhal, potato curry, catahar, men bringing in the 'lotus leaf' for the 'seven curry.' Others bringing in chairs to set up around the 'maaro.' The fences from all the neighbours' yards were removed to ensure a big space for hundreds of guests. This wedding was a significant one as the groom was coming *from away* (Canada). Everyone was telling Maya how lucky she was to be moving to Canada.

The food, fruits, mithai, gulab jamun, peera, were all being prepared for an entire week of celebrations. The ladies from the village were peeling large bags of mangoes to make mango achar and gurumba. Kanchan music *"dulha hain bharati hain"* blaring from the DJ set up on the back stairs. No Guyanese can have a wedding without music and Tassa drums.

Reflecting on that moment years later, Maya would smile. What an appropriate song. Loosely translated, it means *"something is wrong."*

Guyanese Indian weddings typically expand over four consecutive days and begin with a West Indian version of the Tilak ceremony called a *"dig dutty"* or *"maticoor."* The night before the wedding is the *"cook night."* Maya's uncles and the neighborhood men set up the *"firesides"* all along the back wall to prepare for the cooking of the *'seven curry,'* and 'kheer" and "puri.' Maya's female cousins and girlfriends all came out to *"belay the puri'* as the young boys in the village pretended to help the men set up the *'maaro'* and the *'firesides,'* while checking out the young girls. The girls were giggling and jeering at the boys. The boys were trying to hide their interest in the girls from the older, sterner uncles. The atmosphere was that of love and camaraderie with the families — everyone was excited.

The Canadians had arrived earlier that day and stayed at their relatives a few villages east of the *'wedding house.'* They were invited for dinner. Maya's mother had outdone herself, lavishly preparing all sorts of delicious Indian vegetarian food. Although they had to fast before the wedding and were not allowed to eat meat two weeks before the ceremony, the men could have alcoholic beverages. Everything was perfect. The entourage included Jason's mother, father, uncles, aunties, cousins, and of course, the Canadian groom.

As the ladies arrived, Maya glanced up, wondering what they were thinking behind their smiles and laughter. The same reaction, as always, when people saw her for the first time. Maya was always intrigued by her ability to make women admire her, and men behave like fools. She smiled back at her future mother-in-law before taking her place at the dinner table.

The men arrived, her father followed by a train of men from their side of the family, her future husband who was beaming and strutting offensively, when he had less to strut about than any other man she knows. She looked at him, his large frame, curly hair, thinning at the top, and the way he smiled, making him look like an oaf. Maya felt squeamish. She pressed her fist against her lips to hold back the nauseous feeling, to hold back the tears and turn her anger inwards. How foolish she had been to retreat into dreams of a handsome young hero. Maya should have known this day was coming. She should have prepared herself for Jason instead of dreaming all those foolish, silly dreams — Indian movie dreams.

"Hello Maya," Jason took her hand.

She drew away instinctively, startled by her own reaction. Jason interpreted this for shyness.

"You are even lovelier than your pictures, if that is possible." His voice still sounds feminine. Clearly, she had no wish for conversation. She wanted to be anywhere but here.

The families were explaining the details of the marriage settlement. The dowry, the visas, passport, and immigration papers. She was not even listening. The hours that followed were a haze of voices, laughter, loud music, and men drinking "daru." In the whirlwind of festivities with the dancing and singing in the usual Indian style, she had no time for her thoughts. Every night, she was hustled off to bed early by her father's aunt, who insisted that she had to get her beauty sleep. Maya was always relieved to leave the party behind. As she fell asleep, her eyes welled up with tears.

The next day, her grandmother, Betsy, finally noticed her distress.

"I think that the bride needs a little peace." Betsy took Maya aside and was very stern.

"You have to marry him, there is not turning back now. You cannot embarrass your family now; everything is ready to go, so don't do anything stupid," she warned firmly.

Maya was sure her grandmother was thinking of her own elopement with her grandfather because she too had to marry someone of her family's choosing. The story of her marriage to her grandfather is both romantic and sad. That, however, is a tale for another day.

"How silly of me, I was hoping for something better," Maya said sadly.

"It's okay," Betsy said soothingly. "Your destiny is what you make it. God gives us a mind to choose what we want from life. You can make this or break this. It is all up to you." She smiled.

"Hold your head high and be proud. Your children will bring you happiness," She smiled again and added laughingly, "Start soon though so that when I die, they will announce in my death announcement that I have great-grandchildren."

She was always the happiest when someone got pregnant. Maya thought to herself, *she is telling me that God gives us a mind to choose, and yet, I am not allowed to do that. How ironic.*

Afterwards, Gayatri, the maid, came to help Maya get dressed. She watched as Gayatri curled her hair in ringlets, a ritual beautification. She felt like a prized bull before its slaughter. She was dazed and lifeless, just following along, not knowing what she is supposed to do.

Perhaps the most essential day part of the "*Matticor*" is the "*dye rubbing*" ceremony. Turmeric powder or dye is mixed with oil, and Maya was anointed by six young girls from the neighborhood. This had to be done twice, once in the morning and once in the evening. Once the dye is rubbed, Maya could not leave the house's perimeters for fears of nullifying the purification ceremony.

Chapter Two

Arranged Marriage

On the wedding day, Maya's emotions were high. She was nervous, scared, terrified and excited, all at once. Early that morning, Maya's friends came in to dress her.

After the hairdresser finished her make-up, she placed the bindi, a circular red dot with white dots around it. White dots were also placed above the eyebrows, with the areas between the eyebrows remaining empty until the ceremony. The hair was next. It was a high bun with ringlets hanging down the back and sides, as this was the fashion for Indian brides in those days. On the center of her forehead, Maya wore a *'Tikka'* to ward off the evil eye.

The bridesmaids begin draping her saree. It was red and gold. Red is the most auspicious color among Hindus. A large necklace, of uncut diamonds, gold, and gemstones, was placed on her slender neck. Several rows of gold bangles were placed on her small wrists. Premika came in to help Maya put on the '*Jhumkas*' (heavy set earrings), anklets, nose rings, toe rings, and arm bands. The '*Dupatta*' (head scarf) was placed on the bun at the back of her head.

Maya looked stunning. She barely recognized herself in the mirror. Premika and Daya were crying softly as they took in how beautiful Maya looked. With all the glitz and glamour going on around her, Maya remained the central focal point of the wedding day.

Everyone kept saying how late it was getting, that the groom was already at the temple. In Hindu marriage ceremonies, the bride was supposed to arrive first. Maya did not care, she contemplated running away. Where was she to go, though? Everyone knows her family and would surely bring her back home. Before Maya left for the temple, as is the custom, she offered a prayer to the altar of Lord Shiva, the god who protects young girls and blesses them with good marriages. She prayed that he might look kindly at her marriage.

All the villagers were invited to the wedding. Maya's parents spared no expense. Maya arrived with her saree billowing behind her in the crisp morning breeze, the headdress made from gold.

The wedding decorations were spectacular. Everything was magnificent, as is usual with every event Premika executes. Maya's sisters and entire family walked along beside her. An entourage of Tassa drummers and dancers led the way; their joyful wedding tunes a strange contrast to the sobbing of Maya's soul within.

Everyone admired her. What a lovely bride she was. All the guests were pushing to get a look at her. If only they saw the sadness in her eyes. The marriage rituals seem to go on forever. Maya did not understand most of the vows as they were all recited in Hindi, and she only vaguely understood Hindi. The leave-taking was worse. Maya was supposed to go to her husband's home as soon as the marriage was concluded.

Wedding guests were supposed to toss rice and flowers at the departing bride and groom. However, she was not departing yet. 'The Bhariat' (grooms' entourage), *the Tassa* (drums) players and the dancers all lead the way for the bride, groom, and guests to return to her parent's home, where the groom and *the "Bhariat"* were entertained by local singers and dancers while they ate the 'seven curry' lunch.

While the groom was having lunch, Maya was led upstairs to change into her western wedding dress. Her friends brought a small serving of 'seven curry' for her to eat, but Maya was not hungry. They help her to change into a white silk and lace wedding dress. It was beautiful, the bodice embedded with crystals and pearls. Her hair was done up with ringlets and a crystal crown attached to a long veil. As she was about to walk out of the bedroom with her sister, Jason entered.

"May I have a moment with the bride, please," he asked, smiling his foolish smile. Maya's stomach turned as he leaned forward to kiss her. She turned her head away and his kiss landed on her cheek instead.

"You are the most beautiful bride I've ever seen, my friends in Canada will be jealous," he whispered.

His squinty eyes holding hers. He made her uncomfortable. As Maya thought forward to her wedding night, her stomach was in knots, and she felt nauseous. Maya was sure she vomited in her mouth a little. What was she supposed to do? She quickly put the thoughts aside and walked out of the room with him strutting offensively behind her.

As they entered the living room, Maya let him hold her hand to keep up appearances for her parents. Sal was making a toast and offered her a glass of champagne. She never had drunk champagne before.

"Oh, my lovely daughter-in-law, I give you the best birthday gift of all, my son," Sal announced proudly.

Maya almost choked on the champagne. Her birthday was in two days, yet she almost forgot about it. What a nightmare. *Dear god, you are obviously not listening to me*, she thought. This is not what Maya had wanted for her birthday. As they were about to leave for the hotel, Maya finally let go, and could not hold back her tears any longer. She held on to her mother and begged to let her stay.

"I don't want to go," she pleaded.

"Stop crying; you'll mess up your face," her mother sadly. Maya sobbed hysterically and slowly walked out of the yard of her parent's home, saying goodbye to her family as the heart-rendering song 'Mehlon Ka Raja Mila'' played in the background.

It seemed that Jason was in a hurry, while Maya was trying to delay the inevitable. This is not what she imagined her wedding night to be like. The drive to the hotel was in silence. She was not sure if he was upset with her over the hysterical sobbing or if he was as afraid as she was. She assumed he was experienced in sexual activities as he lived in Canada after all.

She was confident that he would know what happened to her as soon as he touched her.

As they entered the hotel, Jason gave the bags to the usher. Their suite was simple, with a lovely dresser and a window with a view of the city lights. Maya went to sit by the window and felt him move behind her, and as he was about to put his hands on her shoulders, she instinctively got up.

"Why don't you change into something more comfortable? I bought you something to wear," he suggested, pointing towards the bed at some flimsy green material.

"Okay," Maya murmured nervously.

She picked it up and went into the bathroom. She locked the doors and put on the shower. The tears came down, and she could not stop. She stayed in the bathroom for what seemed like an hour, hoping Jason would get tired and fall asleep. She tried to put the flimsy lingerie on but could not figure out how to put it on. She was not sure if it was a nightgown, but it was too short, almost to her waist, and did not cover her panties at all. She felt naked and exposed. She nervously entered the room.

He was sitting on the bed, playing with his watch. He rested it on the nightstand as Maya entered.

"My god, you are more beautiful than I ever imagined," he whispered. He got up and led her to the bed. His clammy, sweaty hands undressing her. Her tears welled, and she closed her eyes.

"Can you turn the lights off?" she asked quietly.

"Are you nervous?" he asked.

What do you think, you fool? She wanted to scream.

"Don't you know what to do?" he continued as he walked over to turn off the lights. Maya quickly used this opportunity to get under the covers, but he reached under the covers and groped at her breast, then got on top of her. He tried to kiss her, but she turned away, and he finally gave up. As his manhood entered her, her body felt like a bolt of lightning struck her, and she shuttered and let out a sharp, piercing cry. The pain was excruciating, and she grabbed the pillow and clenched it between her teeth.

Just as quickly as it started, it was over. She lay there, deflated, as he turned over and fell asleep. She hated him, oh how she hated him. How could she ever bring herself to love him like she is supposed to? Maya got up and stumbled to the bathroom. There was blood everywhere on the sheets, on her legs. She was afraid.

Maya sat on the floor of the shower and hugged her legs. She stayed there for a long time as the tears flowed once again. She finally got out of the shower when her legs began to weaken. She felt clumsy, and her back legs and stomach were aching. She lay at the edge of the bed in agony, thinking this was not how your wedding night was supposed to go. As she lay there staring at the ceiling, she eventually dozed off in the wee hours of the morning.

The following day, the newlyweds sat for breakfast in silence. There was nothing to talk about. They left the hotel shortly after and headed for his parent's home. As they were driving along the beautiful coastline, Jason took her hand and kissed it.

Maya flinched. Then she felt sorry for Jason and for herself. Why were they both put in such a sad and uncomfortable situation?

"I am sorry that it hurt so much, it always does the first time, it will be better the next time, and you will be more comfortable," Jason assured her.

I doubt that she wanted to answer, but his words did make her feel better even though she dreaded the thought of him inside her again.

That night, Maya made up an excuse and told Jason that she was still bleeding a lot and in a lot of pain, and that she didn't think it was a good idea. She suggested that they wait until the pain went away and the bleeding stopped. Jason agreed, and he did not try to make love to her again before he left for Canada. He left three days after the wedding, following a small dinner party at her parent's home for her birthday. She was supposed to follow within a month if all went well with her immigration papers.

At the airport, he did not want to leave. Maya's sisters, Daya and Nadia, were there with her. They liked him from the start.

"I will miss you, Maya. I can't wait for you to meet my friends," Jason said, holding both her hands in his. "They will never believe that I have such a beautiful wife."

The word 'wife' kept ringing in her head. Maya, a wife, his wife, she is a man's wife, an awful, balding, offensive boy-man. She was his wife. She could not believe it herself. She wanted to shout at him. She wanted to tell him that she was not coming to Canada. She wanted to run far, far away.

Even though Maya's immigration papers came through within a month, she did not leave for Canada until five months later, prolonging it as much as she possibly could. She really did not want to go, and it was one of the hardest things she had to do. During those five months, Maya was highly emotional. Every night, she cried and cried, not knowing if she would ever see her family and friends again. Maya was afraid to go on a plane by herself; she had never traveled by air before. She felt so lonely and desperate, as if her life were coming to an end, and she had no way to stop it.

One of her friend's, Tilly was feeling so sorry for Maya, and one day she sat her down and convinced her that these last few months were her freedom. This is when she gets to do what she wants. Who knows what to expect in Canada? Tilly advised Maya to be free, and live freely, at least for now. Maya realised how right Tilly was. She had to stop moping around and enjoy her last few months before she left for Canada.

Maya was now allowed freedom rarely given to girls in the village. She was able to go places with her friends. She was able to wear the clothes she loved, the jeans and t-shirts. Maya also began to wear heels. She discovered she loved the feeling of femininity and freedom that high heels gave her. It was exhilarating.

Sadly, that came to an abrupt halt within weeks. The country was getting worse. Many no longer felt safe, fearing they might be targeted just because of who they were or what they do or believe in. Their ethnicity, religion, sexuality, or political opinions. Maya's father, Bali, soon became one of the targets of racial discrimination and political prey.

It was inevitable, so Bali finally left the country. They left at 2:00 am in the morning, no one could know. Premika and Bali had to say goodbye for the first time in their lives, not knowing when they would see each other again. It may be weeks, months, a year, or even more. They were both anxious and upset. All that they worked so hard to achieve, from the time they got married to now, it all may be for nothing. Like many that were fleeing the country, they had to walk away from it all. The atmosphere was extremely tense. These journeys, which all start with the hope for a better future, can also be full of danger and fear. They could be discovered leaving and face prosecution, or worse. They could be discovered leaving their homes or at any point at the airport. No one could be trusted.

It was by sheer luck that Bali made it to America safely. Maya missed her father terribly and slept with his pillows, until they eventually lost his smell.

Maya left Guyana shortly after. It was frightening and upsetting. She had never been away from her family. She could not bear to leave her sisters, she could not bear the thought of being alone, in a new country with a family she did not know. It was one of the worst days of her life. By now, Maya was eighteen. Her mother said she was lucky because she was going to Canada. Maya knew Premika was only trying to comfort her, but she knew she was afraid to send her away, to a strange country, to a different family – she was sending her beloved daughter to a different world, a different life.

As everyone stood at their house in Georgetown on the veranda saying goodbye, a sudden breeze off the Atlantic Ocean a few miles away lightened the air. Maya thought, *I am going to miss this.*

Maya was leaving Guyana without her family, without her sisters, on an airplane, which she had never been on before. Everyone was planting kisses on her cheeks and forehead, and Maya held back tears. Her stomach gurgled as her mother held her tight. The growling in her belly continued when her sisters did the same.

Maya tried not to cry, she did not want her mother and sisters to see her so distraught. They were already distressed with Bali not being there and they did not know when they would see each other again. Maya was heartbroken as she headed for the plane.

Once she found her seat, Maya could no longer hold the tears back. She had seen so much pain in Premika's eyes, similar to when Bali left, and she never wanted her mother to feel that pain again.

All her life, the sacrifices Premika made for her daughters were incomparable.

Maya arrived in Canada on an early summer evening as it was just beginning to get dark outside. Jason was waiting anxiously with his father. He kissed and hugged her, and then quickly whisked her into the car. Everything was so hazy to Maya.

"Are you okay? you must be hungry," he asked.

"I am fine, just tired," Maya answered, looking out the window at the beautiful lights. It was an awesome sight. Everywhere was lit up like Christmas. When they got to his house, Maya was surprised to see so many people. His sisters, their families, his cousins, aunts, uncles, nieces, nephews. Everyone was there. Maya wanted to run and hide. To Jason's credit, he seemed to notice this and told everyone she was tired from the long flight.

"Oh yeah, you want your wife all to yourself," his brothers teased.

Maya felt even more uncomfortable and quickly left the room. Jason brought her suitcase up the stairs and showed her to their room. It was nice and clean, with white furniture and a pink and white bedspread. There was a window at one side with a view of the garden below. There was a sweet freesia smell everywhere. Maya took a shower and went to bed. He joined a few minutes later. As he leaned over to try and kiss her, Maya quickly pushed him away.

"I am sorry, I have my period," she said. This was not a lie; Maya got her menstrual period on the plane earlier that day. It was not even that time of the month.

"It does not matter," he said, groping at the sheets, trying to pull them off her.

"No! It will hurt and besides, I am very tired and exhausted," Maya insisted.

"Okay, fine." Jason got off the bed and left the room. Maya fell asleep immediately. Jason did not push for sex after that. He was genuinely nice to Maya and even took a week off work to show her around, going sightseeing and shopping.

Maya enjoyed it. He did not try to touch her too much. They went sightseeing with his friends and he only touched her when they are taking pictures. They visited all the famous tourist attractions. Niagara Falls, Wonderland, Wild Water kingdom, Centre Island. Maya had her first chicken burger and enjoyed it tremendously, although she couldn't eat the whole thing.

His friends were nice, but Maya was extremely shy, and they teased her for not talking much. They were all loud and seem to chatter all at once. Jason had one girlfriend who went with them everywhere. She introduced herself as his best friend.

Her name was Annie, her family was from Guyana, and she was of Portuguese descent, which explained why she looked Caucasian. Maya remembers Annie looked at her for a long time and said laughingly "You are very pretty, but you need to put on some weight, or you will blow away when the winter hits. Plus, Jason will kill you in bed."

Maya was so uncomfortable with this kind of conversation, but everyone else seemed so open to these things. Maya was not sure how to react. Even though Maya and Jason went out every day, they had to be home in time to cook dinner for everyone. There were a lot of people living in the house. His brothers, their families, his sister, and her family. Maya had to get used to this busy active household. Maya was not accustomed to so many people and they were very loud and noisy, and they all seem to talk at once. Maya never understood how they heard what each other was saying, but she didn't think they cared. They just wanted to chatter all the time. Maya was used to her life back home, where it was quiet and peaceful for the most part. They went to school and temple and occasionally went to the cinemas for birthdays and holidays. Premika and Bali were socialites in Georgetown and sometimes the children were allowed to go the club parties. Maya loved those parties as her friends were also there.

This was totally different. The constant stream of people was never ending. Sometimes Maya would sit in the backyard just to get some peace. Jason would come out to look for her.

"You are being selfish and stubborn," he'd say. "You don't seem to want to mingle with the family, you are not better than them you know."

Maya didn't think she was., she just did not know what to say. His sisters called her a mouse because they couldn't hear her speak. They said she was too quiet. Maya was bought up knowing that girls were to speak quietly and not be loud and noisy. Eventually, Maya's relationship with Jason got into a routine. They had sex every Saturday night. They would go out for dinner every Saturday with his brothers and their wives, his sisters, and their husbands. When they got home, the men would sit and drink. Maya usually went to bed. Jason would come up and they would have sex and then he would go back down to join the men. It was like a duty to him.

Maya never understood how things worked in his family and she never tried to understand either.

Maya tried to find a job, but since she was not educated in Canada, nor did she have work experience, the only job she could find was at a Cassette factory.

This was about the time that Jason started talking a lot about sex. He started asking weird questions about what Maya thought about other men and if she would ever try a threesome. Most of the time, Maya just ignored him and other times she would tell him that those were not the things you discuss with your wife. Maya never thought he was serious. Maybe it was just his way of making conversation.

When Maya finally started working, she went through so much racial discrimination. She hated being called a "Paki." She tried to explain to the ignorant people that even though she is brown, she was not from Pakistan. They did not understand, they did not know, nor did they want to know, they just saw Maya as brown and labelled her a 'Paki."

She could not believe that there was so much ignorance when it came to different cultures and races. Maya gave up trying to explain her culture or where she was from. Most times, when she said, "I am from Guyana," she would get a response like, "Ghana? You don't look African."

"No, Guyana, in South America," she'd respond.

"Oh, you speak Spanish then."

"No, broken English."

"What language is that?"

At the end of the summer Maya started school, taking computer classes, Human Resources and Business Administration.

Chapter Three

Different Strokes ...
Different Folks

Maya loved school and made friends with some other girls her age that were in the same classes. Altea was from Ukraine, Lizzy was of Italian descent but born in Canada, and Janine was Chinese Canadian. They had lunch every day at the pub at the end of the street by the college. They ate pizza and calzones. Maya tried getting used to this, but to this day she does not like pizza. They talked about their families, boyfriends, and high school days. Maya was the only one married, and eventually she told them about her loveless marriage. They could not understand why she would stay in a loveless marriage instead of getting a divorce. Maya knew that they would not understand how much she would embarrass her parents to even contemplate such a thing. Her mind was corrupt, confused, and unstable, from soaring hopes and dreams to wondering why she ever got married. Wondering why the Indian tradition of arranged marriages still exists in some Indian families in Guyana. Why did some families stick to this tradition, while others did not? Maya thought, *why did my family have to be so traditional?* Yet, she loved her family values and how their values were strong regarding religion and culture. Maya and her sisters kept up the culture admirably and followed in the footsteps of their parents and fore parents. They were heavily involved in dance, singing, cultural plays, and shows every week.

However, since she came to Canada, Maya, who was an ardent Indian dancer, had to give up all those things. There were no avenues to exercise such cultural activities where she lived.

At this point, Maya was getting uneasy and unhappy. She knew that she was born to do better than this, that her life had to have more meaning than this mediocre existence. She found herself asking the question her friends did, *why should I stay in such an unhappy marriage instead of getting divorced?* Even though she knew that they were right, she still argued with her friends.

"Plenty of couples stay in marriages that look miserable from both the inside and the outside," she claimed.

Yet, when she was alone, she found herself contemplating her other options, because she was so unhappy, so miserable, and so dispirited. In her marriage, it was easy to see only the negative. In doing so, she may not desire, let alone take the time, to assess whether her marriage was unhealthy or just unhappy. She felt that the distinction is critical for taking the right course of action for her, for her family's reputation, for her in-laws, and for her husband. Yet, she knew that she did not enjoy their time together. She did not feel heard, and she did not truly listen. They did not have sex or did so only infrequently. Maya eventually started fantasizing about life without Jason.

She plucked up enough courage to finally talk to Jason about it. They had spent a lovely day at Niagara Falls with his parents, but Maya was even more sure that she did not want this life. She wanted a home of her own, a place she could call her own. She wanted to be independent, not living under his parents' roof, and it seemed that it would be like this forever. She wanted to do things and go places on her own terms, not only when the family decided they should. She wanted to dance again, to be free. Maya wanted to explore things on her own, not with the entire entourage. Sometimes she thought this dream of a private life was selfish, and then she remembered that her present life had no privacy, no time for her to be alone, no time for her to dance anymore.

She knew that this was not her life.

She was living a life that Jason and his family wanted, not what she wanted.

That evening, while watching TV, she asked him out on the balcony. She was cautious with her words and even asked him if he would be willing to move with her. She had contemplated this many times and thought that if they were alone, in their own place, with their own lives, maybe their marriage would be happier, healthier.

But Jason was livid.

"Are you out of your mind?" he asked. "Are you not a true Hindu as you claim to be? You damn well know that it is our duty and honour to stay with my parents, and to take care of them when they are old."

Looking back at this now, Maya cannot help but smile at the irony of this. Jason's family and Kyle, their eldest son, now take care of him!

Jason continued his argument, but Maya was not listening to anything anymore. All she heard was that he wanted a son.

"As an Indian woman, you are supposed to have a son by now, to carry on our family name, our legacy. Plus, "coolie" people don't abandon their parents, not like white people," he continued.

Maya eventually backed down on the divorce, she wanted a son too. She was positive that this would change her life and make her much happier here. Maya made the decision to stay in the marriage. She did, after all, marry for better or worse, and knew that she did not want to disappoint or embarrass her parents. Or her in-laws, for that matter. She started to daydream about her life with a son, a beautiful baby boy that she could spend all her time with. She knew that babies required hard work and dedication. Yet, the arrival of a new baby is fascinating. Newborns represent new life, new hope, and the promise of love. That's all she wanted now.

To her utmost joy, Maya became pregnant that summer. It was the most amazingly wonderful news in her life. She was overjoyed, and it showed. For the first time since she came to Canada, she was happy. She was glowing with joy and pregnancy. She kept hearing it confirmed everywhere she went — she was radiating. It made her feel beautiful, and she noticed that she had an exciting smile all the time. Her nails started to grow faster. Since she came to Canada, she had cut her long mane of dark hair short. Now, almost immediately, it was getting long again.

That celebrated glow continued to grow during the second trimester. Looking in the mirror, she saw that her skin looked brighter, and she had a radiant look, and her breasts were noticeable bigger. Maya could not help but show off the new look. Jason, too, seemed to be loving the new Maya — and the new physique. He took notice of her sensuality, her blossoming breasts, and soft curves. Despite the morning sickness, she was the happiest she had ever been since coming to Canada.

Four months into the pregnancy, without warning, her happiness was quickly diminished. Jason gave her the biggest shock of her life. He asked her to do insulting, rude, horrifying things. Insane beyond anything she ever imagined, not even her nightmares were that bad. She could not believe her ears.

They had just returned home from having a wonderful dinner with their sisters-in-law and brothers-in-law at a well-known Chinese restaurant downtown Toronto. Maya had showered and was sitting on the bed, massaging the bottom of her feet, as they were so sore. They had taken the Go-Train to Toronto, and there was some walking involved.

Jason came out of the shower and dropped the question.

"You want me to have sex with your brother!?" she responded in disbelief. "Are you crazy??!! Are you out of your mind?"

Maya sat down slowly on the bed in total disbelief. She could not believe this was happening.

"It is not so bad, everyone in North America does these things, it is common," he tried to encourage her.

She looked at him, and she was suddenly reminded of this hellhole that she lived in. It will never end. Her small moments of happiness were like a dream amid a horrible reality. My God, she thought, this is her husband, the man who vowed to protect her, no matter what.

The man she lay beside every night, the father of her child. Her head lowered in disbelief and shame. Tears were streaming down her face.

Then she looked up at him again, thoughts racing. She realized that he never respected her, he never loved her, and that he did not care anything about their unborn child. Then another thought struck her... Oh, my god! He must have discussed sexual things about her with Mark, his brother. She could not bear to think such horrible things.

"It will be okay, now is the best time, you can't get pregnant because you already are," he persuaded.

Maya was horrified. He wanted her to get pregnant! He was waiting for this! She instinctively covered her stomach with her hands to protect her unborn child.

Maya realized now why his brother had been looking at her lately in such a strange manner. She never felt so unprotected, displayed, and unloved, as she did at that moment. Her stomach was not showing yet, but her breast had double in size, and she realized that very evening, Mark could not stop gazing at them. But at the time, she had not given much thought to Mark's behavior. She had gotten used to the fact that she had the power to make men behave foolishly. Her resentment and anger were building. She felt so angry, exasperated, intensely irritated, and frustrated all at the same time. The images in her mind left her shocked and stunned at such cruelty to her pregnancy.

Jason came on the bed to sit beside Maya. He tried to put his hand on her arm, caressing it in a creepily persuasive manner. She got up and shoved him away from her.

"You have got to be kidding me!" Her anger was apparent.

She wanted to grab his throat and squeeze the life out of him. She wanted to strike him so that he would come to his senses. She ran to the bathroom and did what she had not done since she got pregnant. She locked the door and dropped to the floor in disappointment, sobbing hysterically.

Jason knocked on the door several times.

"Maya, open the door!" he demanded.

She ignored him. He continued knocking and insisting that she opened the door. She continued to ignore him, the hysterical sobs not subsiding.

"Maya, open this fucking door before I break it!" he challenged.

He began to bang louder. When that did not work, he started to push the door with his shoulders, but he didn't have much strength to break them.

He continued swearing loudly now, "Maya! I said open the fucking door now! I will fucking break it, I swear! Don't fucking push me, I'll fuck you up."

His shoulder was hitting the door in a constant thrusting motion. Maya was so terrified that he would hurt her and the baby. She pressed her back up against the door, her legs pushed up against the bottom of the toilet bowl to give her some resistance and leverage. Her sobbing subsided as she concentrated all her energy on keeping Jason from getting in.

Jason's mother, Kayla, must have heard the commotion. Maya heard her asking Jason, "What's wrong babe?" Her tone was always soothing when she spoke to Jason.

"Why are you behaving like that? Why is Maya locked in the bathroom?" she continued.

Before he could answer, Maya shouted, "I am not feeling well, and he won't leave me alone!"

Maya knew she could count on Kayla to get him away from her. Kayla was always kind to Maya and treated her like a daughter. They had this special bond, and Kayla took Maya under her wing when she came to Canada. They would shop, garden, and decorate the house together. Their relationship was a pleasant one.

Kayla immediately proceeded to scowl Jason.

"What the heck is wrong with you? She is not feeling well, and you treat her like this?" she scolded.

"She was fine earlier," Jason replied defensively. He had stopped hitting and pushing at the bathroom door.

"Don't you know that some women experience severe mood swings during pregnancy?" she offered. "They can make you go from being happy one minute to feeling like crying the next. You need to leave her alone."

Kayla came close to the door, "Maya, take your time, I will make sure he stays away tonight, get some rest."

They both left. Maya heard retreating footsteps but waited in the bathroom for close to an hour before venturing out. She quickly closed the bedroom door and fell on the bed, exhausted with a terrible backache.

Maya did not talk to Jason for two days and continued to avoid him as much as possible after that. She was like a robot, walking around dazed, feeling exposed and bewildered. As weeks went by, Jason did not mention his request again, and Maya assumed that he was over his stupidity and idiocy. They avoided each other most of the time, and Maya's gloomy mood had subsided. Christmas was approaching, and this was the best time of year for Maya. She loved decorating and making Christmas cakes, just like her mom used to back home. Two weeks before Christmas, Mark's wife, Janie, left for Guyana that morning as, sadly, her younger brother had passed away of Malaria. Mark and his kids came to stay with the rest of the family at the house.

Great! Maya thought. One big happy family.

She loved the children and did not mind helping to take care of them. She didn't care much for the adults. Mark was off work, as was most of the men in the family. She was never sure what they did for a living, but they never seem to have regular hours, although they did seem busy enough with all the comings and goings and borrowing each other's cars. Maya did broach the subject with Jason once, and he said Mark had a construction business and most of the men worked with him. But from Maya's point of view, all of them were mostly just hanging around all day, pretending to be busy.

From the time Mark arrived, his attitude towards Maya was disconcerting. He seemed mesmerized. It appeared that he could not take his eyes off her. His gapes and stares were unbearably sinister. It made her so highly uncomfortable that she stayed in her room most of the time or spent a lot of time with the children. Maya always felt more comfortable with the children. She took them for walks and winter fairs to get away from the busy household. Everyone was starting to arrive for Christmas week. Maya's sisters-in-law and their entire families from New York, Florida, and Stratford were coming to stay for the holidays. The noise and bustle of the arrivals were too much for her. She was suffering from severe nausea with the pregnancy; the smell of all the food, especially the meat, made her sick. She tried to get out of the house as much as possible.

Jason saw how sick she was, and he seemed genuinely sorry for her. At times, he would take her and the children for drives in the evening, but that made her even more nauseous. Jason suggested that they spend an evening at Mark's house. Since Mark was at their house, his place was empty. They would have a chance to have some peace. She jumped at the opportunity as she desperately wanted some peace and quiet. Jason quickly arranged for this to happen on Saturday evening. They were going to order Chinese food and watch a movie. Maya was a big fan of action and military films.

It started as a beautiful Christmas evening, they arrived at around 6:30 pm and it was already dark outside, the Christmas lights from the neighbor's house twinkling in the lightly falling snow. They ate dinner in mostly silence before they started to watch a movie. Maya was getting a bit uncomfortable with her pregnancy. Even though she was not showing, her stomach felt huge because of her petite frame. She wanted to put up her feet most of the time, so she settled into the sofa. But she was not comfortable enough, so she turned and lifted her legs on the couch to rest her back on Jason's larger frame. She shifted her weight so that her head was on his shoulder. He reached around and rested his arm on her stomach. She felt comfortable. They had never done such things before as there was always too many people at the house. Her body tension eased, and her back felt relaxed. She settled down to watch the movie. About halfway into the film, Maya was sure she heard a noise, but Jason quickly reached for the TV remote and turned up the volume. Then he leaned over again, this time, for his gun on the coffee table. He placed it closed to him. She sat down again, contended to watch the movie. She was not alarmed by the gun at all. Maya had gotten used to seeing the men in the family carry guns. It never occurred to her that this was not normal.

As they continued to watch the movie, she heard a noise again, like keys jingling.

"I heard something that time, didn't you hear it?" she insisted.

"You are jumpy, learn to relax," he whispered, pushing her back down on the sofa.

Suddenly, the door open. Mark stood in the doorway, his shirt was open to his waist, and he was gazing hungrily at Maya. A feeling of sheer fear gripped over her. She knew something terrible was about to happen. The look of gleefulness on Mark's face confirmed the sinking feeling in Maya's heart, and it did not feel right. She turned to Jason, almost in a panic, but he was smiling as if he too knew that something was about to happen. Something he wanted to happen. Maya's heart sank.

"What is he doing here?" she demanded, terrified at the answer. "I thought you arranged for us to be alone."

"It's the man's house, and he can come and go as he pleases!" Jason answered, and they both started laughing. Maya hopes for Jason to save her, to reassure her that all was well, failed. She collapsed onto the couch.

Mark was walking towards the couch, his intense gaze never leaving her body. She tried to get up, but Jason grabbed her and pulled her head towards his lap. Maya's body was halfway off the couch, her legs on the cold marble floor. Mark grabbed her legs and pushed her up on the couch. With one hand, he held her legs together, and with the other, he was undoing his zipper. Jason was above her head. He grabbed her arms and held them over her head. She struggled to look up at Jason, her eyes pleading for help, but Jason was laughing, enjoying himself.

Did he see the terror in her eyes? Did he see the fear in her eyes, the sheer horror? Did he know she was about the let out a terrifying, sickening scream?

He must have sensed this because he quickly put both of her small wrists in one of his large hands, and with the other, he stifled her scream. Maya's body was sliding against the leather couch as she struggled to get out of their grip.

Mark's legs were on top of hers, making it easier for him to move his hand over and push her dress up around her neck. She felt stifled as his clammy hand moved over her breasts. She could feel his satisfaction and tried to scream once more.

"If you fucking scream, I am going to shoot you bitch, so shut up and take it like a lady," Mark growled.

Maya's eyes quickly roamed for the gun. It was in Mark's hands now. Fear and terror overcame her. Maya's mouth was dry and sore from Jason's hands. Tears were streaming down. Her face hurt. She shut her eyes and prayed, "Dear Lord, this cannot be happening. I am having a nightmare. This has got to be a nightmare."

Maya's soul seemed to have lifted from her body, and she watched from above as they raped her. First Mark, then Jason. She watched as her body did not struggle any longer. She was lying there, taking the assault, as though her body did not belong to her. As if she was dead. She felt nothing. She was lifeless, powerless. Nothing, no feelings, no hurt, no emotions. Maya felt out of her body like she was no longer a part of it; she was just an onlooker. She just watched as these monsters battered her body. She was powerless against these beasts.

When they were done, they got up, and Mark left.

Jason must have gone to the kitchen. Maya could not tell what was happening. She was too confused and numb. Slowly, Maya felt her soul re-enter her body. She got up, feeling dazed, exhausted, numb, desensitized, and insensible. There were no tears, no pain, nothing. Just utter humiliation and shame. She did not believe... She could not believe what had just happened. She slowly walked to the shower, ran the cold water, and just sat on the floor of the shower, her arms hugging her legs, still wearing her soiled dress, with the cold water running down her head and body. She sat there, shaking profusely, for almost an hour. Maya's body was tormented, agonized, by this horrible unmentionable nightmare. She could not even think. She was blank.

From that moment, she was no longer Maya. She was a stranger, even to herself. She was left in a state of fear and anxiety. Jason came out of the kitchen while she threw her jacket on and frantically ran to the door. Her hair and clothes still wet, she was shivering, her teeth chattering.

She was so cold and frightened; she could not stop her upper and lower teeth from clacking against each other. She so desperately wanted to go home. She wanted to run, hide from these monsters. Yet she had no place to go, but home, where they all lived. She could not go to her parents. Mark and Jason would kill her if she did. She could not go to the police, or her family would be killed.

Jason ran out behind her.

"Take me home," she said urgently, without looking at him.

He did not say anything. She quickly got in the car, and they drove all the way home in silence. Looking back now, Maya could not imagine how she got the courage to run out of that dreadful place.

They got home within a few minutes. Still no tears, nothing except a dull numb feeling in the pit of her stomach and a bad taste in her mouth. They pulled into the driveway and Jason put the Jeep in park. He knew she could not get out on her own, the jeep was too high, and she needed help down.

He turned to her and said, "Look here, I am sorry about what just happened, but if you tell anyone, you'll be sorry not only for yourself but for your family. Do you understand?"

Maya nodded, silently. She did not look at him as he helped her to the house. No one saw them come in as they were all in the living room drinking, playing dominoes and cards. Loud laughter and chatter echoed through the house.

Maya quickly went upstairs and immediately got into the shower. She wanted to scrub everything away, as if the hot water would erase what happened.

That night she did not sleep, and many more sleepless nights followed. She could not sleep, she just kept thinking about Jason's threat. She knew what he meant. Mark was heavily involved in things Maya was unaware of, but she suspected that they were involved in something illegal. Their meetings were always in the basement, and she had never paid much attention.

That Christmas was the worst of her life. In the weeks that followed, overwhelming and persistent sadness seemed to overcome her. She started to feel a sense of hopelessness. Even little things were making it difficult for her to cope, to carry out meaningful activities, and she continually felt a sense of despair.

For months after this, Maya would wake up screaming from horrible nightmares. Jason would cover her mouth and make her go back to sleep. She stayed awake, afraid to fall asleep again.

Maya was sure his parents heard her and probably thought she was psychotic, but they never said anything to her or asked if she was okay. Life went on with Maya in solitary most of the time she was at home. One day, she was reading a book and saw the quote "When a person can't find a deep sense of happiness, they distract themselves with pleasure." She thought to herself: this baby will bring me that sense of happiness and pleasure. She was determined to find meaning in her life and change her perspective about the horrible experience she had suffered. She knew that she could not raise the child alone, nor would they let her leave. They would take her child, and she would be dead.

Maya thought that if she worked on a project that demands her attention and artistic skills and abilities, it would distract her from the scary, sinking feeling at the bottom of her stomach. She started to paint a mural of Disney characters on the wall of the bedroom for the baby. Then the day finally arrived. The festive atmosphere in the waiting room coupled with the gleeful smiles carried by families that were all present, the mothers and fathers from Maya and Jason's side were all there. Maya became fully dilated after a long seven hours.

Jason went out to the waiting room to share the news that the baby was coming soon. They became silent in anticipation.

The echoes of crying from the newborn baby broke the calm silence. It was a boy!! They named him Kyle.

Maya was deliriously happy. The miracle of giving birth after the nine months of mixed emotions, anticipation, constant lower abdominal pains, backaches, and the horrid experience of sexual abuse, were now a blurred memory as she looked at her son.

I am now living in the present moment and learning the true meaning of unconditional love, she thought.

Premika and Bali came as soon as she was admitted to the hospital. Premika understood very well what her daughter was experiencing.

"It seems like just yesterday when I gave birth to my daughter," she said to the nurses. "My grandson has brought back the memories of being a young mother. My daughter is so naïve not knowing how to breastfeed, bath or even hold the baby."

Motherhood has been a challenging task in every way, and Premika knows what her daughter feels. Being a mother brought her to the edge so many times, but this only made her stronger, more courageous and more patient.

Maya could not admit how scared she was during the last four months of her pregnancy. Her greatest fear was whether the baby would have complications, whether it would be an average child, or whether she'd have difficulties during birth with all the stress experienced during her pregnancy. She could not bring herself to tell Premika any of this. Maya had so many conflicting emotions. At first, she thought it would be strange and she didn't think she would want Jason around, but his presence gave her the emotional support and courage to endure the labor pains until delivery.

Chapter Four

Realization

Kyle's birth brought new meaning to Maya's life, and she put all the horrible things behind her. She was the happiest she had ever been. She had a newfound purpose to protect this child with her life. Maya looked down at his tiny little fingers and toes. His eyes were dark. He was so beautiful. She held him in her arms, and the more she looked at him, the more she fell in love with him. It was a love that was so overwhelming, but in the best possible way.

Maya couldn't understand the constant smile Kyle brought to her face, but she learned to appreciate that the feeling would allow her to be happy again, to live in the moment and enjoy the simple things in her life. She honestly didn't think she could love him more. Maya remembered her grandmother's words and thought, *she must be so happy to have a great-grandson, finally.*

It was time for Kyle to get a Hindu name. Hindu families rely on Vedic astrology to arrive on the name of a child. This is called *"Naam Samskara or Namakaran Samskara"* (the naming ceremony of a newborn).

It is traditionally believed that a boy's name should have letters in even numbers (2, 4, 6, 8) and girls should consist of odd-numbered letters (3, 5, 7, 9), but 11 is considered the most promising length for both genders. Hindus believe in selecting a child's name based on his or her birth star, which depends on the child's birth date, time, and place. After consultation with the Pandit, Kyle's Hindu name had to begin with D, so they give him the Hindu name. "Devanand."

Maya stayed with her parents the first week after delivery, as is custom in Indian and West Indian families. She was surprised that Jason even allowed this, but quickly realized that he had an ulterior motive for agreeing to let her stay with her parents for the week. She learned that two days after Kyle was born, Jason's brother-in-law, Clement, had received a call that his father had passed away. The entire family was going to New York for the funeral, so Maya would have been left alone. She didn't understand why Jason had to go; he was not even related to this man. He insisted that he was going and left, saying Maya must stay with Kyle at her parent's place until he returned. Maya was happy about this. She felt she needed her mother anyway. As Premika said at the hospital, she did not know how to bathe the baby, feed the baby, or even change the diaper. Kyle was her parent's first grandchild, so they were happy to be doting grandparents. Maya spent the first three days there, not expecting Jason back until the weekend, so she was very surprised when he called to say he was coming home. His tone was rude and obnoxious.

"You'd better be there with my son when I return," he demanded in a threatening tone.

Reluctantly, Maya's father took her home.

It wasn't long before the abuse became a regular thing — emotional, verbal, physical, sexual — it was like an addiction to Jason. Maya was afraid of him. She feared his wrath. She became afraid to have sex, and even more afraid to speak to anyone about this. Their relationship was built on control and submission.

Looking back, there were lots of tell-tale signs early on. One time, long before Kyle, they were supposed to meet at Jason's workplace at the Eaton Centre downtown, so that Maya could get a ride with him home instead of taking the train. He did not like her taking the train alone. In hindsight, Maya realized he was afraid she would make friends on the long train ride home. So instead, they decided to meet at the food courts. Maya waited and waited, and eventually, she walked away, thinking maybe he had forgotten. Just as she started to walk into the train station, she saw him waiting. He was furious and grabbed her purse, chucked it down on the ground, and yelled at her in front of everyone, saying "you're so stupid, where were you, I was waiting for you for so long!"

Maya was so scared. He thought he was right, and she was wrong, and there was nothing she could do. She felt helpless. She cried the whole way home and he tried to explain his reaction by saying, "I love you so much, I worry about you so much. You are a stranger here in this city and if anything happened to you, I would not forgive myself."

Shortly after that, he quit his job at the Eaton center and started working "construction" with Mark.

And it never stopped. One day she was playing with Kyle on the bed when Jason came home, appearing like he was drunk. For no reason at all, he started accusing Kyle and Maya of making a mess of the bed. He picked up some objects and threw them at Maya, slicing her knee. The excuses he gave her this time was that his anger came from him being overtired. He said that he was not adjusting to working with Mark, and it was causing him emotional upheaval.

Jason liked to control everything, and he thought it was what husbands should do. Maya felt she was a prisoner in her own home. She felt like a dog on a chain, and she couldn't get off. She was married, and she was unhappy. Jason was violent and did not treat her right, and he didn't treat her family right either. He got nastier and nastier. Every day, things just got worse. Maya was becoming more withdrawn. She feared making any decisions for herself, worried he would be displeased. Even her clothes had to be chosen for her. Jason had begun withholding access to money, and ultimately, her independence. Maya was not allowed to go anywhere alone. It was either him, his parents, or his sisters that had to accompany her.

When he spoke to her, it was with contempt, resentment, and belittlement.

Maya was afraid that if she left, she would not have financial security. But she feared staying, too. She wondered how many couples who place great value on financial assets were willing to overlook their dissatisfaction in their marriage to maintain their lifestyle.

But Maya didn't care about her financial status. She was more concerned about her social status — for her, for her parents, and for her in-laws. Divorce changes everything. In Indian culture, divorce is out of the question because of religious beliefs and family values. Both families believe that the kids are better off with both parents together.

Kyle was 10 months old when Maya finally decided it was enough. She had called the police so many times to the house, but they were all in vain — Maya did not have any witnesses as Jason's family were all still living with them. They would deny it every time, and because she had no physical marks, the police never believed Maya. Jason was clever with his attacks. He never hit her where she would bruise. His attacks were on her stomach, he would throw her on the floor and kick her until she passed out. Sometimes he would grab her by her neck and choke her until she could barely breathe. Other times, he would continuously punch her in the stomach. To this day, Maya has a broken upper left rib, but at the time she did not know it was broken.

Maya went to see a lawyer — unknowing to Jason, of course. A colleague from work had recommended him. She sat down with the lawyer and told him her whole heartbreaking story, and his words cut like a knife.

"Either you stay and learn to live with it, or you get out now. But there is no way you will ever be rid of him because there is a child involved," he said, somberly.

Maya realized she had no case as there still hadn't been an arrest. She became more and more afraid that Jason would out what she was doing, fearful that he was having her followed. But finally, after another fight, she snuck out and sought advice from the police, disguising herself with a wig and sunglasses as not to be recognized.

"I have a friend whose husband has been beating her up," she said to the police officer, covering her face with a scarf. "What can she do without getting him arrested?"

"She can come in and make a report," he answered, looking at her as if he knew she was talking about herself.

"And what will you do?" she asked.

"Well, we will arrest him."

"And then he gets bail until it goes to trial?" she asked.

"Well only if there is enough evidence," he offered. "Sometimes these things never get to trial."

"So, he gets arrested and then bails himself out and he is free to do whatever he pleases," she retorted. "She pisses him off by getting him arrested and there is no protecting her if he comes after her."

"Well, she could get a restraining order..." he answered, noticing how upset she was becoming.

"What is that? A piece of paper to throw at him when he attacks her again? What about the kid?" she almost shouted.

"There's a kid? Sorry ma'am, but that's for family court to deal with," he answered quietly. She walked away before he could finish. Maya knew she needed to do something. She couldn't live like this anymore. Either she runs far away, or she stays and deals with it. But she knows deep in her heart that there is no running. Jason would find her. She had no money and nowhere to go.

Jason was always genuinely civil to her after his bouts of anger. One time, when it was close to Valentine's Day, he mentioned that would be nice if they went away. She was not going to agree to it at first. In fact, she blatantly refused. But after a few days, she thought it would be nice to get out of the house. She told him that she would go.

"Nope, you lost your chance, I offered, and you said no. Plans changed," he said mockingly.

Maya did not mention it again. However, they did go out for dinner on Valentine's Day with his family, as usual, and they had "Valentine" sex that night for the first time in a very long time.

After a few weeks, Maya withdrew even further and started to get even more depressed. She was profoundly unhappy. The only time she felt joy was when she was alone with Kyle. He was such a happy child, his smile lit up the whole room. And when he laughed, you could not help laughing with him. Maya's heart overflowed with love for him, and he knew it. He only wanted to be with her. This, however, was not always possible as Jason's parents, for some reason, did not think she could handle taking care of him, and they were constantly interfering.

Jason's father was always trying to tell her what she should or should not do. She wanted to take Kyle off the bottle as soon as he could hold a cup, which was exceedingly early as he had developed motor skills at an incredibly early age. By ten months, he was talking and walking. Kayla was against the thought of the baby eating solid food and giving up his bottle.

"My Jason, sucked on my breast until he was six years old and look how healthy he is," she used to say.

Yes, and that's why he is also overweight and sick in the head, Maya wanted to reply. But she never did, she had too much respect for Kayla, and Maya knew that Kayla didn't know any better. That was how she was raised and that is how she raised her own children. Sometimes Maya felt sorry for Kayla, all her life, from such a young age, she was oppressed by Sal.

Not long after Maya realized that she was pregnant again. It came as a surprise, as she could not recall how and when she got pregnant, but it must have been on Valentine's Day.

Things appeared to be getting back to normal with her and Jason, and he was gentle and kind to her whenever she was sick in the mornings. Jason stopped abusing her both physically and emotionally, and even sometimes stopped to hug her when she was cooking. Although it was an awkward and self-conscious feeling, she was beginning to trust him again. They even started visiting her parents on some weekends once more.

One time, Maya and Jason even spent an entire day with her parents, her sisters, and their families. It was so beautiful, and everyone enjoyed playing and fussing over Kyle. Jason did not even nag her to leave early.

They went home around nine that night, and as they pulled up on the driveway, Kyle insisted that she carry him into the house. Maya had been trying not to lift him too much as he was heavy — it was not good for the baby. He was pleading, though, and so she agreed. As she was carrying him up the pathway, she suddenly slipped on a stone. Her feet give way under her, and she fell. She tried to save Kyle from hitting the ground and, in turn, landed on her side with a thud. She felt a sharp pain rip through her whole body, and she let out a scream. Kyle must have sensed her fear as he, too, let out a cry, even though he was not hurt at all. Jason quickly grabbed him and helped her to her feet. They went inside and did not even mention to anyone that she had fallen. Jason took care of Kyle as she took a shower and relaxed.

After Maya put Kyle to bed, she went downstairs to join the others. They were playing cards and wanted another player. She did not like playing cards and did not even know too much about it. She agreed to play after much coaching from Jason's nephews, whom she got along great with. They always were on her side whenever Jason was abusive and would even lock her in their rooms when he got physical. She sat down and became engrossed in the game when suddenly she felt a hot sensation between her legs, as if she had urinated. Maya was puzzled and then jumped up in her horror. There was blood everywhere. She was so scared yet embarrassed all at the same time. She just stood there, looking at everyone looking back at her in shock. Jason's sister, Karen, quickly got up and helped her up the stairs, with Jason following along closely. She helped her into the shower and stayed there for a while, but the blood just kept streaming down her legs. It would not stop. Maya was terrified.

"I think you should call the ambulance," Karen said.

Jason quickly dialed 911. Within 15 minutes, she was in an ambulance and on her way to the hospital. Maya had never been more scared. As soon as they arrived, the nurses and doctors were already waiting for them. They put her on a gurney, and she was rushed to intensive care. There was so much going on around her, her temperature was taken, then her blood pressure, pulse, blood tests — everyone rushing around in a frenzy.

Finally, she was taken to a quiet room in the intensive care unit. Luckily, she had great benefits from work and was able to get a private room. As Maya lay there, waiting for the results to come in, the bleeding continued, but it was more contained now. She prayed and prayed and prayed, asking God to forgive her. She was unsure if she wanted to bring another child into her unstable life, but now that she thought she may lose the baby, she was determined — intent on saving her. She prayed for the baby's safety. She must have prayed until she fell asleep.

"Mrs. Singh," Maya heard voices that sounded so far away calling her.

She opened her eyes to see the doctor, his stark white coat, a sharp contrast to Jason's dark clothing. Jason and Karen were there as well, standing beside him.

"Hello, Mrs. Singh, my name is Dr. Patel," the doctor said, peering over his wired framed glasses. "You are a fortunate woman," he continued with a gentle smile.

"Why?" she asked, rubbing her eyes.

"The history we obtained from your doctor, coupled with the observations we have made today, have raised several concerns. We still can't figure out how you did not lose this baby with all the blood that you lost. We have several preliminary diagnoses, so we would like to keep you here for further observations. Do you have any questions or concerns at this time?"

Maya was too dazed and dizzy to comprehend what he was saying. She shook her head instinctively touched her stomach. "No, Doctor."

"Do you know the sex of the child?" The doctor asked.

Yes, she replied quickly. "We found out only last week."

"Well, you're going to be just fine, and you have a very strong and determined girl in there," he was looking over to Jason, who smiled nervously.

"Thank you, doctor," he said, seemingly unsure of what to say.

"Mrs. Singh, I suggest that you get some rest now. You are still very fragile. You must take it easy and not overdo anything yet. I will see you in the morning."

The doctor smiled and left. Jason and Karen came over to the side of the hospital bed.

"I am going to go as well. Jason will stay with you," Karen said.

"Thank you so much," Maya replied tiredly, "You're very kind." She was falling asleep again.

"I will go too, it's no use me staying," Jason said hurriedly. "You know how I hate hospitals."

"It's OK. Take care of Kyle and tell him mommy loves him, and that I will be okay," Maya yawned tiredly. It was probably 3:00 am in the morning by now. She was ready to sleep.

The next day, the doctor came to see her. He assured her that she was going to be okay. He suggested that she follow up with her own doctor immediately. He recommended that she stay off her feet until she saw her doctor.

Jason called the hospital to speak to her, and she told him that it was okay for her to go home. He came an hour later to pick her up. He didn't even bother coming into the hospital. She met him at the entrance, with the orderly pushing her out in a hospital wheelchair. She felt weird and uncomfortable in the wheelchair, being pushed by a strange man. The following day, Maya saw her gynecologist. Even he thought it was a miracle that she did not have a miscarriage. From that day on, she was determined for the child to be safe. She was hell-bent on ensuring that no harm will come to her baby girl. Especially from Jason, from his abuse. Maya's fears mounted with every day that went by.

Now that Kyle was over a year old, he was becoming increasingly active and inquisitive. He was so intelligent, and his curiosity would get the best of him, which made him "in trouble" more often than the other cousins. If there was ever a cup on the table, full of anything at all, and they did not catch him in time, it was all over him and the floor in a matter of seconds. If there were stairs around, he was up the entire flight before you could catch him. He would see you are coming and run fast, dashing the other way, giggling all the while. It was exhausting, and a tiny part of Maya could not wait until this phase would pass.

Maya recalled one time, when Kyle was about two and at his cousin's birthday party, he was playing in his usual playful manner in the playroom with all the toys. He would not stop going up the stairs and then back down, and in and out of all the rooms. Maya's sister-in-law, Cindy, had a son the same age as Kyle, but the total opposite in personality. He just sat on a couch and played with his Legos, bursting into tears if anyone looked at him. Cindy was looking at Kyle running around, and Maya could see the disapproving look in her eyes.

Realization

"Wow, Kyle's a real a handful!" Cindy said in a sarcastic tone.

Maya smiled and said, just as sarcastically, "Yep, he's your typical 2-year-old."

Maya's gynecologist had ordered complete bed rest for the rest of the pregnancy. Since Kyle was such a "handful," she suggested to Jason that she go stay at her mom's so that she could have help with Kyle, but Jason flatly refused. After much debate with his family, they finally decided to send her to stay with his older sister, Leena. Maya eventually agreed. It was much better than staying at this house wondering if she would have to endure the same horrible experience she had when she was pregnant with Kyle.

In addition, Maya could not be away from Kyle. Even though she knew she could not take care of all his needs at the time, Maya wanted him with her anyway. Jason's sister Leena agreed to have Maya and Kyle stay with her and her family. Since she was a housewife, she had time to watch over Maya and Kyle.

It was happy news for Maya, and she was excited to be away from Jason. However, this happiness didn't last long. Jason decided he would come with them as well. Even though Leena only lives a block away, he was not going to let her be alone. He was not going to take any chances with her alone with anyone else. His insecurity was increasingly disturbing.

Maya could eventually go home to her family as the end of her pregnancy neared, and she gave birth to their baby girl, Melena, in November. It was blissful and beautiful. However, unknowingly to Maya, she was suffering severe post partum depression. In the weeks that followed, overwhelming and persistent sadness seem to overcome Maya. She started to feel a sense of hopelessness. A hopelessness that made it so difficult to even want to spend time with the children. Little things were making it harder for her to cope. It was exceedingly difficult to carry out meaningful activities with them as she continually felt a sense of despair.

Maya started to doubt if she could do anything right and inwardly criticized everything she did for the children. It did not help that the family was also very critical. This led to much frustration that perpetuated into a downward spiral. Her self-esteem was at its lowest point, combined with self-loathing and suicidal thoughts creeping in daily.

Maya's loss of interest in favorite activities, like watching Bollywood movies on Saturday night, slowly affected the children.

Maya's lack of focus, combined with poor concentration, began to hamper her job performance. She once had so much dedication. She had achieved so much in the past eight years of working at one of the most prestigious and well know Telecommunication companies in Canada. Unfortunately, this brought on negative thoughts. Often, she would put the kids to bed and go to bed herself before the sun even went down.

She even began to dislike going out, unable to be social appropriately. She was irritable and short-tempered. She did not even want to visit her parents anymore. She stopped asking Jason if her and the children could go for their weekly Sunday visits. She started to lose interest in her friends at work. Eventually, her avoidance caused an immense sense of isolation, and the symptoms of depression worsened. Maya's lack of energy due to the sadness led to insufficient sleep. She continuously felt unwanted and unloved, and started having panic attacks and bouts of anxiety at work. She could barely get out of bed. After work, she would clean up the dishes and head straight back to bed, blaming migraines.

On the outside, their marriage seemed normal. But behind closed doors, she had nothing to do with Jason, physically and emotionally, and he left her alone. Maya realised that she was in a downward spiral. She could not go on like this, she had to make herself happy – at the very least for her children. She had to shake this. The children needed her. Maya went to see her doctor, who prescribed anti-depressants, but Maya was determined not to take any medication. She did not want to get dependent on medication. She decided to have a long talk with Jason. She told him that she wanted to leave but had decided to stay because of the children and because she knew that Kayla and Sal could not live without them. This seemed to genuinely concern Jason. He promised to be more supportive and attentive and even allowed her to have a credit card and pocket money.

She started visiting an aesthetician to get her eyebrows and her upper lips waxed. She began receiving regular manicures and pedicures. She loved how her hair had grown and began changing her hairstyle often. Maya's hairdresser suggested highlights, and she agreed. It had been a long time since she felt this good, and Jason seemed incredibly pleased with her new appearance. For some unknown reason, she still wanted to please him, to make their life as normal as possible. Despite all that happened, Maya wanted this family life to work — to be contented with what she had. She was getting a lot of compliments from friends and family. She thought, if we continue to avoid each other, this could work.

Life was quiet for a while, and then Mark returned. He had been away, and Maya just assumed he had moved away — she had never bothered to ask where he was. Part of her honestly thought he was in jail. Maya realized that her newfound happiness could be snatched away from her dramatically.

She was about to return to work after some time off and had just got both children out of diapers and away from bottles. They were growing healthy, happy, and strong, and were brilliant kids. Kyle was always looking out for his little sister. It was such a joy to watch them together. One day, when she was at home alone with Kyle, Melena, and their cousins, she was sitting on the porch watching them play on the front lawn. Suddenly, a silver SUV pulled up on the driveway. Who steps out but no other than Mark!

He walked up the walkway, looked at the kids on the lawn for a brief second before turning his attention to Maya. Her heart sank, her body trembled in fear. At that moment, she knew that her peaceful life would never be the same again. She looked up at him in disgust, hopefully hiding her fear. But, instead, he just stood there, staring at her, as if undressing her with his eyes. Maya had never felt so uneasy and uncomfortable. His creepy stare made her shutter in revulsion. Finally, she got up and headed for the kids, but she was stopped by Mark, his hand on her upper arm.

"Where is everyone?" he asked in an authoritative tone.

"Let go of me." Maya tried to sound just as an authoritative. He let go.

"I asked you a question," he demanded, his eyes never leaving her.

"I don't know. Go ask your sister, she lives just up the street," Maya answered back quickly, hoping he would leave.

"You are looking very beautiful these days," he said gapingly.

"Thanks," she responded politely and proceeded towards her children.

"Be nice," he shot after her. "We don't want those beautiful children getting hurt now do we?"

Maya shuddered at the thought of him hurting her children, but continued to walk towards them, pretending she did not hear.

"Come on kids let's go for a walk," she offered to children.

"Oh yeah, all the way to the store? Can you buy us ice cream, mom?" Kyle asked excitedly.

"Sure, sure why not?"

Maya dusted the grass off Melena's dress, and they started towards the convenience store. She could feel Mark's eyes on her. Later that evening, she mentioned her encounter to Jason and how he threatened the kids. Jason quickly tried to dismiss her fears.

"You take everything seriously; he must just be joking. *I am* sure he did not mean it the way you think," he said.

Maya tried to bury her fears, but it didn't take long for Jason's attitude to change once again. He became aggressive, abusive, unbearable, and pejorative again, as if Mark's presences made him a completely different person. He started hitting her again and even threatened to hurt their family if she complained to anyone. She knew his involvement in all the illegal, illicit activities was increasing alarmingly as he was away quite often. However, she was glad that he was away and was also fearful of saying anything that would upset him or trigger his temper. When he was home, his behavior became stranger and stranger: he would constantly talk about Mark as if Mark had a hold over him. Mark said this, Mark did this, Mark wants this, Mark likes it this way... Mark, Mark, Mark. Maya wanted to scream, *"Shut the fuck up already!"*

When he was not doing this, he asked her what she thought of other men, other men's bodies, or if she would like to sleep with them. Or how would she feel to have another man, sometimes even referring to his cousins. It was disgusting, offensive, and appalling. It was as if he was taunting her to see if she was attracted to other men. *How sad*, she thought.

Once again, life had become miserable and despairing. Maya's short-lived moments of bliss were snatched away from her again. It was as if God was playing a sick game. He was teasing her with happiness and taking it away again. Eventually, she suggested to Jason that they should not have any more children. He did not argue or put up any resistance. However, he refused to have a vasectomy and insisted that she had a tubal ligation, but life went on and they did not immediately follow through with this plan.

Chapter Five

Artificial Happiness

Maya's reservations around Jason's family were increasing, and she was consumed by depression most of the time. But, as the days went by, she came to realize that the way you hope your life will turn out is not always the way it does.

Life had started to feel normal again. Maya was doing a great job at work and got promoted to supervisor at one of the leading telecommunications companies in Canada. Kyle had started kindergarten, and Melena was a sweet and happy child that everyone loved to babysit. Kayla and Sal especially loved taking care of the children. Maya was so busy with both work and the children that she did not realize she had missed her period two months in a row.

On a cold winter morning, Maya was driving to work sipping her coffee as she battled the heavy stop and go traffic on the Don Valley Parkway — usually called the Don Valley parking lot for the typical almost halting traffic. The realization came out of the blue; she could not remember the last time she had her period. Maya shook the thought. That day, she kept working, but on her lunch break, moving as though on autopilot to the drugstore, she bought a two-pack of pregnancy tests and prayed that she would not run into a co-worker in the checkout line. Finally, she came back to the office peeing on the little stick in the first-floor bathroom, knowing it was the one that was normally always empty. Maya waited a few minutes, idly thinking about what to make for dinner that evening. Then she stared at the faint pink plus sign and sat down on the toilet in disbelief. Maya did not want another baby right now. She could not handle this responsibility. She was not ready to do it again.

She spent the rest of the day feeling slightly numb, like she had just heard life-changing news about somebody else, except it was her life.

Maya toyed with the idea of not telling anyone, not even Jason, for a couple of days. Tests could be wrong, she told herself. But a part of her understood that she would have to retell this story to his family, and then to her family, and pretend that they were a happy couple expecting a third baby. Maya should be stoked about being pregnant again, but she wasn't.

She felt ambivalent, and she quickly learned that showing even the tiniest sliver of uncertainty about the baby would lead to a double-edged societal sword. For Indian women, there is a strong set narrative around female attitude and behavior when it comes to pregnancy.

Maya felt frustrated, sad, and very anxious — and then guilty. What if something happened to the child as punishment from the universe for not being grateful enough for this experience? Why did she get pregnant when she knew so many other women who desperately wanted to be in her shoes right now? Shouldn't she feel more, well, lucky? Shouldn't she be happier?

Maya thought, if she ignores it, puts it out of her mind and doesn't think about it for a while, she could remain calm... But she started feeling sick and nauseated just thinking about it, so she went to see her doctor.

After doing another pregnancy test, he announced, "You're pregnant" with a smile.

Well, that confirms it, she thought. *I am not ready.* Maya's mind was racing.

As the weeks went by, she became increasingly anxious and depressed, so the doctor eventually ordered her off work. However, staying home made her feel even more unhappy. Maya longed for a place of her own, a quiet place where she could raise her children the way she wanted. One to love and take care of them her way.

She even started to miss work and hoped the doctor would give his consent for her to return to work, even though she knew it would take her away from Kyle and Melena during the day. After several visits and tests, the doctor finally said it was okay for her to return as long as she kept off her feet. This helped her keep her mind off things, and by this time she was about three months pregnant, the morning sickness had somewhat eased up, so she could work for most of the day without interruptions. In the evenings, Jason was helping her with the baby, but Kyle only wanted Maya.

"I want mommy do it," he would say to his father's offers for baths and bedtime. "Make bubbles." He smiled. Kyle loves baths.

One Sunday, when Maya was about four months pregnant, Jason agreed to take her to visit her parents. This was a rare occurrence, many of Maya and Jason's fights centered around not being able to see her family. However, she was optimistic that he just wanted to announce that they were having a girl. They had only found out just last week at the previous ultrasound. Maya was overjoyed that it was a girl. A boy and two girls would make the perfect family. Little did she know she was in for a lot more than she bargained for.

Maya was always tired when she got home from work and tried to spend most of her time with her children whenever possible. Once again, as usual around Christmas, the house started to fill up with people and family members coming to stay for the holidays. Maya desperately wanted some solitude, and even the children seem to be tired of all the excitement.

Mark came to stay with them again. Unbelievably, Janie was in Guyana to attend another family funeral. Maya was not even sure if they were telling the truth or if they just sent her away. Maya even thought that maybe Janie made it up to get away from Mark. Then she quickly shook that unkind thought away.

For some odd and outrageous reason, Jason thought Maya would agree for them and the children to spend a night at Mark's house. He insisted that it was so that Maya and the children could have some time to rest.

Immediately, Maya panicked.

"Are you out of your damn mind? Do you think I would fall for that shit again?" she asked in disbelief. "Do you think I am still that stupid young girl that you and your brother took advantage of?"

"Understand there's no way I'm ever going to that house again," she continued. She could not believe what she was hearing. Was she imagining this? What happened before was still unbearable.

"You know Mark has moved into a new house, right?" he offered as if that would make a difference.

"Jason, you are crazy!" she cried. "I don't even want to discuss this."

"Come on, you really think I will hurt you again, or let anyone hurt you? I know that I have not always been a good husband, but I am a good father, and I would never let anything or anyone hurt my children."

"Damn it Jason! You know what, that is it!" she flung the kitchen towel on the floor she was drying the dishes with and looked at him. Her disgust must have shown on her face.

"All the years of being with you, I've tried extremely hard to make this work," she burst out, almost yelling. "The sacrifices I've made, the things I have put up with, the rape, the abuse, the violence, the things I've forgiven you for. When were you a good husband to me?"

"I didn't tell anyone, I didn't report you or Mark, and yet, you don't seem to see that I am a faithful and dutiful wife?" she continued, shouting now.

"Calm down," Jason grabbed her hands and held her close, not wanting everyone to in the house to hear Maya's declarations.

She tried to remember a single moment he was a good husband to her. She could not. It was all for him, all about him, what he wanted, where he wanted, and when he wanted.

Maya looked at Jason and she knew that she never loved him. In this moment, all she felt for him was pity. He did not know how to love a woman; he did not know how to be happy and content. He is a follower, a follower of Mark. A follower of his family. He was Marks's puppet. Jason would never be a leader. She pitied him, felt sorry for him. Yet, Maya had to admit that he would not do anything to hurt his children. Even though he was atrocious, brutal, and horrible to her, especially before becoming pregnant, he was not abusive anymore and had stopped making lewd suggestions about other men.

When she arrived at work later that day, there were twelve red roses on her desk with a note that read, "I am sorry, it is only for you and the kids, I would not have asked."

When Maya got home that that evening, Jason asked if she had gotten the roses and if she thought of his idea, his suggestion. She said she was too busy at work and did not have the time. Jason seemed unconvinced.

The next day, there were 12 more roses on her desk with another note "Don't forget to think about it." Her boss walked by her office and said, "Hmmm, another bunch of 'make-up' roses, he must be in the doghouse." Maya was so embarrassed.

Chapter Six

Rude Awakening

One thing about Jason is that he is very persuasive, and despite everything, Maya was still not strong enough to resist it. Jason knew he could wear Maya down if he kept on pressuring her.

She started to think, is he going to do this every day? So, she finally did give it some thought. Maya knew it would be good for her — she wanted to get out of the house, and she figured if the children are going to be with them, it should be fine. Jason would never hurt the children, and she would have some time alone with them. They could have some well-deserved peace and quiet, like an average family would, even if it were just for one night. She convinced herself that it would be good for all of them.

So eventually, she agreed to go. They decided on Friday night after work. Jason would meet her there with the children, and they would have a nice quiet dinner and watch Barney movies. She packed a few things for the kids and stuck them in the truck of her car that morning and then left for work. That evening when Maya arrived Jason was already waiting for her at the door.

"Where are the children?" she asked, starting to go back down the stairs.

"I had an important delivery, I couldn't take the kids with me," he answered quickly, referring to what Maya assumed was one of his many illegal escapades.

"They are on the way. Ivan will be here shortly with the children, no need to worry," he continued. Ivan is Jason's nephew.

Maya felt queasy. She immediately started breathing heavily. How was she to know it was not another setup that Jason tricked her into.

"Don't get hypered," he assured her. "They are already on their way; they will be here any minute now."

She was fatigued and very hungry, and she desperately needed to shower. Jason quickly took her bags and hustled her inside.

Maya felt woozy and wondered if she was doing the right thing. Her mind told her to leave, but her body refused, exhausted and drained, she just wanted to lay down. She had been working at the computer all day and was dying to put her feet up.

"I'll take a shower in the meantime," she suggested, thinking at least she would be done by the time they got here.

"I'll order pizza for us," Jason suggested.

"No pizza, it gives me heartburn," she replied quickly. "Maybe we can go out for Chinese food when the kids get here. I am not sure if I am comfortable here after all."

In her mind, Maya was debating whether to stay at all. She quickly took a shower to clear her mind. She contemplated the whole situation as she showered, and suddenly felt even more terrified. She was slowly losing her nerves and realized that she could not stay. She quickly got out of the shower and into the dressing room.

The house was silent, so she assumes the children were not here yet.

She got dressed quickly and went to the living room, where Jason was on the phone.

"Where are they?" she demanded to Jason.

"They must be just around the corner," he quickly answered, noting her distressed look.

They both seem to pause for a moment. Jason seemed to be waiting for her reaction. Maya's heavy breathing was loud and very apparent in the quiet room.

And then the door swung open, and to Maya's dismay and disbelief, Mark was standing at the door. Her heart sank. *Oh my god oh my god oh my God*, her head was spinning. It hit her like a ton of bricks. The realization that the children were not coming after all was too much to handle.

Maya fainted.

When she came to, they were in one of the bedrooms and Mark was on top of her. She let out a piercing scream and immediately felt a sharp pain across her face. He slapped her.

"Shut the fuck up and you won't get hurt bitch!" he leered.

He was naked. Maya tried to shift out from under him but quickly realize her hands were tied to the bedpost above her head. She screamed again.

"Help, help me please!"She felt a sharp pain across her forehead and realized he had struck her with his gun.

She froze. The piercing pain across her face was unbearable, her head was throbbing,

"He said shut the fuck up," Jason yelled from across the room.

She looked at him pleadingly but saw the look in his eyes, the gleeful delight. He was enjoying this.

Maya felt an awful sickening feeling settling into the bottom of her stomach. She was nauseous and woozy, her head spinning. She felt as though she was reliving her worst nightmare. Because really, she was. She screamed again.

"Help!"

But Mark was already pressed up against her. Her body shivered in humiliation.

"Stop moving, bitch," his face so close to hers, she could smell the garlic in his breath. "Not another fucking word from you, or you'll never see those lovely children of yours again."

Her body cringed in shock. The fear... the dread and depression she had been living with all this time, none of it compared to how it felt now, her worst nightmare had come true.

This cannot be happening again, she thought in horror. *Surely, I'm dreaming a horrible, sick dream.* She tried to get up, but they grabbed her legs and held her down.

"Don't fucking fight this. You know it's going to happen. Put your hands on my muscles, enjoy it, touch them," Mark sneered. He took her hand and rubbed it against his chest.

She must have fainted again.

The next time she woke up, Jason was on top of her. She tried to move, shifting her body, left to right, trying to wriggle from under his weight. He pinned her down with his legs. Her arms were beginning to get numb from being tied above her head.

She wanted to scream for mercy.

Her head was still throbbing, the pain was excruciating. She closed her eyes and willed herself to breathe. She felt a cold object against her temple and slowly opens her eyes, and her heart stopped for what felt like forever. It was the gun! Mark was holding it against her temple as he leaned into her face.

"Your fucking brains will be on the floor bitch. You will fucking die," he sneered. "You'll die if you keep fighting like a fucking bitch."

"Just shut up the fuck up and do what you are told!"

"Did you forget the last time, bitch!" he continued.

She stopped struggling, she closed her eyes again, willing herself to be in another place. Dreaming of a beautiful garden with butterflies and sweet-smelling roses. In this dreamland, Kyle and Melena were happily trying to catch the butterflies. Maya knew she had to live for her children, and for the sweet unborn child inside her.

Tears ran down her face, she bit her lips hard to fight back from screaming.

Gardens with butterflies and sweet-smelling pink roses. She kept forcing herself to think about Kyle and Melena and how happy they would be among the butterflies.

Maya passed out again and had no idea what happened next. Finally, she opened her eyes to Jason standing over her, naked.

"Go take a shower," he said roughly.

She tried to get up, but her knees buckled under her.

She fell back. Jason grabbed her arm and held her up. Her legs were wobbly.

"She's a fucking spitfire and built like Miss America," Maya heard Mark say mockingly.

"Boy you are lucky she does not put on weight," he continued as they talked about her like she was not even there. They seem engrossed in each other. Jason lit a cigarette and passed it to Mark. She grabbed her clothes and darted for the bathroom.

"You're a fucking lucky man," Mark said again.

"You want to?" was all she heard Jason say before closing the bathroom door and turning on the shower. But Maya did not shower, she just let the water run. She just wanted to get the hell out of there. She tried to dress, so she picked her pants up and tried to find her underwear. Her bra must have fallen on the floor in the living room, she couldn't find it anywhere.

Leave it, she told herself. She pulled on her sweater and quietly opened the bathroom door, cautiously moving towards the dressing room. She had to walk past the dressing room, the master bedroom, and the kitchen before she could get towards the side door. As she eased past the other bedroom to make her way down the short flight of stairs, she caught a glimpse of something and could not believe her eyes. It was Jason. And Mark was having sex with him... from behind!

Maya froze, her feet betrayed her, and her body shuddered in disgust. She could not believe her eyes. She quickly realized that they did not even see her standing there. They seemed to be in a world of their own. She quickly ran towards the door and realized she did not have car keys or her purse. She recalled leaving it in the kitchen. She crept back towards the kitchen and grabbed her bag. She swore that she knocked something over on the countertop. She didn't bother, she just ran out the side door quickly, not bothering to look at the disturbing scenes in the bedroom again.

She fumbled with the keys, her hands trembling. Then, finally, she got in the car, but her feet were shaking so badly, she could not keep in on the accelerator.

She took a few deep breaths before she could drive and tried to stop herself from throwing up. She drove and drove to nowhere, now sobbing hysterically, trembling, her body shaking uncontrollably. She looked around and realized she did not know where she was. Then she suddenly realized that she was on a dirt road somewhere.

She pulled over and wiped her eyes. She took a few deep breaths and turned the stereo on to play 'Hanuman Chalisa."

She thought of Kyle and Melena, and the fright took over again. *Oh God*, she thought, *they will get the children!*

She turned the car around and headed back west.

She turned up the stereo louder and blasted the 'Hanuman Chalisa.'

She did not know how, but fortunately she reached home safely. She ran into the house.

"Kyle where are you?" she called. "Melena!?" No answer. The house was eerily quiet.

"Where are you honey?" she shouted, she was beginning to panic.

"Hey, what's going on?" Danny, Jason's older brother, was standing at the top of the stairs. He was on the phone.

"Why are you yelling?" he asked, leaning over the railing at the top of the stairs.

"Where is everyone, where are the kids?" Maya asked.

"They are over at Leena's. Everyone went there for dinner," he said.

Maya remembered that they were invited for dinner at Leena's. One of the reasons she agreed to go with Jason to Mark's house was to get away from this. From all the noise, drinking and crowded spaces.

"Ma and Dad did not see you guys come home so they took the kids," he explained. "What is wrong, are you okay? You look like hell!"

"I am... am.... Fine," Maya stammered, her voice breaking. He noticed. He always has been kind to her and her children. She always felt like he was sorry for her.

For a moment. Maya wondered... should she tell him what happened? She contemplated for a moment.

No, she shook her head. *This is not your own family ... no matter what, they are one clan. They will stick together.*

"I'm not feeling well, it must be the pregnancy," she offered as she started up the stairs. Danny came down and help her.

"Why are you shaking? You look like you've seen a ghost," he said.

"I don't know why I feel like this," she lied.

"Do you need anything?" he asked.

"Yes, can you go over and bring the kids home?"

"And I would love a cup of tea and some Aspirin," she answered, her head was pounding from the blow. "I have a massive headache. It may help."

"Okay, I'll see if Ma has any Aspirin," he offered.

"She has some in the medicine cabinet in her bathroom, I'll take a shower in the meantime," Maya replied.

"OK, I'll make the tea for you, and I'll knock on the door when it's ready," he said kindly.

Maya shut the bedroom door and went to the bathroom. She took her clothes off and got into the shower. She sat on the ledge in the shower. Her body was too weak to stand. Her mind was racing. She wished she were not there, that she could just disappear. She didn't want to be here anymore. She wanted all of this to end... Right now, right this moment. To end it all.

She got out of the shower and got dressed. She opened the bedroom door, and the tea and medication were on the floor in the hallway. She picked them up and closed the door again. She opened the bottle. She looked up at the mirror, two pills in hand, and took them followed by a big gulp of tea, which was already cold. Then she took three more, then another one, and then another. Maya kept filling the water from the tap.

It's just medicine, she thought, and then she realized what she was doing. She looked up again in the mirror and saw her face and pregnant belly, and she realized the consequences of what she was doing.

She quickly stuck her finger in her throat and vomited. She threw up everything; her mouth had a bitter taste now. She was exhausted, but she wanted Danny to bring the children. She was scared that they were not there at Leena's house.

She went downstairs, but they were not there. Danny was watching TV. She did not want to go get them herself, she couldn't bear the thought of mingling with the family.

"Hi Danny, are you going to get the kids for me?" she asked.

"I thought you may want to rest," he said, lowering the volume on the TV.

"Please, if you don't mind, I want to put them to bed, before I go to bed," she begged.

Danny agreed to go get them, but by the time they got back, she was asleep. The next day she woke up with Kyle leaning over her trying to pry her eyes open with his fingers. Melena and Danny's son Vinny were jumping around on the bed.

"She is awake! She is awake!" Kyle was shouting, then started to jump up and down as well.

Maya jumped up.

"You were asleep when they came in." Danny must have heard the commotion and peeked his head in the doorway.

"You asked for tea and for me to get the kids. I put them to bed so you could rest, you didn't look too good last night," he offered. "I knocked on your door, but you did not answer."

"Oh," she muttered lamely. She slowly sunk back into the pillow. Her head hurt, and her stomach ached.

"What have I done?" she thought.

Jason came in but didn't say anything. He just went straight to the shower. He did not push her to get up. The kids settled in on the bed and they watched TV. Maya was not even paying attention to the cartoons or the commotion. She was unsure what to do. She wanted to pick up the kids and run away, but she knew they would find her. Her stomach churned. She could not think straight. She was so confused and tired... So tired. Not to mention humiliated and disappointed. *Why, why, why did I let this happen to me again,* she thought in utter shame. *Why did I believe Jason again? How could I have been so stupid?*

Maya wanted to kick herself.

She knew they would not let her leave with the children, and she could not leave them here.

My parents will be so embarrassed, she thought. *What will their friends think, what will the people at the temple say? I cannot afford three children on my own.*

Things went on as if nothing happened. Maya was too terrified, too scared to tell anyone what happened. Jason never said anything, and she did not bring it up all. The fear of losing the children was unbearable. She was terrified to even think about it. She started acting normal, with nothing to alert anyone of her thoughts.

In the weeks that followed, Maya knew that she had to start making plans to leave this home, but she knew she could not just pick up and leave. It would take months to plan, to ensure that they would not come after her, her children, or her family. Not until now did Maya take an interest in what Mark and the rest of his gang did, their activities, their whereabouts. Any information she could gather. She put in a request at work to install a landline in her bedroom so that she could consult with a lawyer privately. Maya started having conversations with all the 'clients' from Guyana that were staying at the house. She paid attention to every action. She was buying time until her pregnancy was over.

She started listening to every word they said. She even formed a relationship with one girl who had a baby a bit younger than Melena. She heard the "gangs" conversations from the basement. Her bedroom was above, and she could clearly hear everything — their plans, their schemes, every deal, every stake and even their sick jokes.

Maya learned quickly. She had to put her plans into action as soon as the baby was born.

She had to escape, but she had to plan for it. She was never alone with the children. Kayla and Sal were always there.

As soon as the kids were in bed, she retired too. To listen....to learn...... to know. This was Maya's only escape. And learn and listen she did. She had known that Mark was the mastermind, the leader, the *"kingpin"* of this illegal, illicit business. She was mortified at all the things that were happening right under her nose. She felt like she was living in an awful gangster movie, like a twisted version of "Married to the Mob." It struck her suddenly – they are like the mafia! That is how they made their livelihood and all that money. She realized how all the brothers and sisters had huge mansions, new luxury cars.

Because Maya had been so naïve all this time, she continued to pretend to be this way. No one knew that she been watching and listening to them. Jason continued pretending that he was doing "construction' errands, and she pretended to believe him. Instead of construction, they were making fake passports. They even had a passport making machine and were using actual passwords of their families and friends and were even buying passports from persons willing to sell it for the right price. They would then change out the photos to match the person they were bringing from Guyana. They were illegal alien smugglers. The entire family and the 'gang' were all using their nicknames and aliases from back home when they were on the phone making their plans, their deals. It was almost as if they knew they were being watched or listened to. Mark held meetings every evening in the basement after dinner. Every week, the 'clients,' as he called them, were being brought from Guyana. These clients would stay at the house for a week, or two, then be taken over to the US through various borders.

When Maya questioned this, convincingly she was told that it was their family from Guyana. They were trying to migrate before the immigration laws changed. At the time, Maya knew that life was getting much harder in Guyana. The struggles in a country that did not seem to be getting any better were real. Everyone wanted to migrate to either Canada or America. It was the norm these days.

Other 'clients' were brought with their own passports, applied for refugee status, then a few weeks after their government assistance income kicks in, they were taken to the US. Mark would then continue collecting the government assistance of these people even though the fee for one person to come from Guyana and be taken to the US was approximately USD 15,000.

Maya remembered one specific occasion where she overheard that Jason's older sister Dina was going to Guyana to take the "fake" passports to the potential client. She heard them talking about how nervous she was, and Mark told her not to worry, that he knew someone at immigration in Guyana and they will take care of her when she gets there. Maya recalled how she thought that Dina must be crazy to do such things.

What Maya learned horrified her, yet, she never told anyone, not even her mother. Maya had a routine, she would come home on time to have dinner with everyone, play with the kids, bathe, and read to them before putting them to bed. Just in time for when the men would retire to 'play dominoes' in the basement. She would make excuses that she needs to work, or she was tired, and would head up to her room as well. The things she heard left her sleepless most nights.

She made her escape plans as she continued working until the last day of her pregnancy.

Chapter Seven

Deflated Joy

M aya sometimes wondered how Jason allowed her to work. She was the only one who worked in this house. She did ask him this once.

"How come you let me work? I know you guys are against it, none of you work," she questioned.

"You're right!" Jason said with a laugh. "None of us work, that's why you have to."

"Don't you think people would wonder where we're getting all this money from?" He continued. "That is why you must work! And don't try anything stupid at work, we have people watching you there as well."

Maya had suspected that. She had seen the same guys that hang around the house, hanging around her workplace cafeteria. She knew he had people watching her.

But Jason's confirmation of what she had suspected gave her anxiety every time she saw them. Her friends at work noticed it too. As her pregnancy progresses and she continued to work, Maya stops staying so late and started paying more attention to what was happening at home. As Maya's pregnancy progressed, her blessings were that her mother-in-law took good care of the children, and by the time she got home from work, they were already bathed, and fed. Maya spent her evenings reading to them and putting them to bed.

Her second daughter, Ryder, was born on a bright Sunday morning. Maya's labour was very intense, and Ryder was breached, with both legs coming out first, during delivery. This caused severe anxiety for Maya, as the doctors dislocated Ryder's hips while trying to assist the baby's delivery. For months, Ryder had to wear a "splint" over her diapers.

However, the birth of Ryder seemed to give Maya extra strength and courage. Courage to leave, to finally start a new life with her three perfect babies.

Being home on maternity leave aided Maya's plan to learn more about Jason and his family's illegal operations.

The horror that Maya saw, the brutality, the callousness, the cruelty, and cold-bloodedness was unimaginable. One night, Maya heard a muffled moaning and thumping sound coming from the basement vents. She quietly crept downstairs. As she reached the doorway to the stairs, she almost fell from what she saw.

Two men, who she had never seen before, were punching, beating, and smashing their firsts into a young lad whose hands were tied to a chair behind his back. They had covered his eyes with a black cloth, and his face was covered in blood. She balked at this horrible scene. She was terrified, and as quietly as she came down, she ran back upstairs and straight to the bathroom. She could not keep down the nauseating feeling and vomited in the toilet bowl. She felt sick to her stomach. She was so afraid; she went back to bed and covered her ears with her pillow. She must have drifted off to sleep in the wee hours of the morning. Maya said nothing to anyone the next day. She did look downstairs, but there was no evidence that anything was amiss.

Over the next few months, what she saw was out of a gangster movie. What these beasts were doing was unimaginable, mind-boggling, and beyond belief. They were turning huge men into crying babies. They were extorting and threatening people. She saw them in the basement, she heard them on the phone. She saw them leaving in the wee hours of the morning and sometimes not coming back for days. It seemed that the entire family was working for Mark. It also dawned on her that there was another woman in the picture, Mark's mistress, Roselle. It seemed that she was the one who was actually calling the shots. She was the "Boss." She would drop off the visitors and picked them up the following week. She would bring food, snacks, and drinks for them. Maya's stomach was constantly in knots. She had anxiety attacks daily. She worried for her children.

But leaving with the children became much more challenging than she imagined. Sal and Kayla were always there, and they never let her go out alone. She knew it was going to be difficult. Maya was living in a dangerous world. She contemplated leaving so many times, she made so many plans in her head, but she couldn't carry out any of them. Only in her head, it was easy. Maya knew she could never leave her children behind. She knew they would find her, and they would torture her, just like they did to the young lad. They would make her pay. They would kill her. Even worse, they would harm her family.

She thought of Jason's older brother Jay's wife. Many years ago, the family had taken the children, her two boys, away from her. They left her like a madwoman to wander the streets back home, crying her heart out for her children. The same two sons were now working for Mark.

Maya thought of Mark's wife, Janie.... Janie feared Mark, and Maya soon realized that it was because of her fear of him that Janie would not speak to anyone. She would always sit at family dinners and gatherings without saying a single word. Everyone thought that Janie was snobbish and rude, but Maya knew.... she knew that Janie was scared — maybe even terrified. Janie had to know more of her husband's secrets than Maya ever would. She must know what they did. How they made fake passports, smuggled illegal aliens and drugs, how they exercised extortion with whoever tried to stop them. She must know everything. Maya wondered if they had done horrible things to Janie, too. Was she raped like Maya was? She wanted to reach out and ask her, but she was too scared. Maya wasn't sure she could trust Janie to speak openly to her.

Maya was beginning to get very depressed again. All her thoughts were focused on getting away from the house with her children. She decided that going back to work early from her maternity leave was the best option to put her plans into place.

Everyone at work was so excited when she returned to work, but they immediately sensed her despondent attitude. They could sense her withdrawal from social activities. They kept telling her to smile, to say something. At home, Jason also seems less interested in her and spent more time with Mark and his "friends." Yet, when he was home, he kept on being abusive.

Soon after Ryder's first birthday, Maya told Jason that she wanted to leave, and he should go with her. She thought maybe if he left with her and the kids, he would change, he would be a better person, a better husband, and they could have an everyday family life. He did not seem surprised at all. Maya tried to discuss this several times after that. Every chance she got with Jason alone, she would bring it up, but Jason would change the subject or walk away.

Maya knew he would never leave; she knew she had to get the courage to do this on her own.

Maya started speaking with the lawyer on her lunch breaks and paid several visits to his office. She knew she had people following her, but she did not care.

Maya had reached a certain point where nothing mattered except the safety of her children; she knew she had to get them out of there, and it had to be fast. It was their only chance of a decent life. Maya was worried that Kyle would learn this unhealthy, dishonest, unlawful environment.

Maya no money to pay for the lawyer, and she did not qualify for legal aid. She was too ashamed and humiliated to ask her parents.

Several weeks after she returned to work, the lawyer called.

"I am really sorry, Mrs. Singh, but I have to hold off on seeing you for now."

"Your account was very much overdue, and until you pay something on this, I have no choice but to hold off. Do you have any savings?"

"Sadly, no," she said apologetically.

"You should save something at work, you can do it," he encouraged.

"There is no way," she said. "Jason knows every deduction from my paycheque, he knows how much should be there."

It was no use, he waited outside her work to take the paycheck from her at 10:00 am every other Wednesday morning when she got paid. Even if she tried, she could not get away with any money.

But little did Maya know; she was about to get unexpected assistance.

It was early Monday morning. Maya had just gotten back to her desk from grabbing a coffee in the cafeteria. Sally, the front desk reception came back to her office and peaked her head in.

"There are some suits here, asking for you, I put them in the board room," she smiled with a wicked twinkle in her eyes.

"Suits?" Maya asked.

"Men in suits," Sally laughed.

"I am not expecting anyone," Maya replied, puzzled.

She got up and followed Sally to the boardroom. Four men were standing around a large table, all dressed in dark blue suits. Two of them had third hands behind their backs, bodyguards, while the other two looked at pictures on the wall.

"May I offer you some coffee or water?" Sally asked the 'suits' as they turned to greet Maya.

"No, we are good," answered one of them, who looked like he was in charge.

"Hi, I am Maya Singh, Human Resource Department Supervisor," Maya introduced herself and shook each of their hands.

"I am Insp. Pierce, Chief of Police, Durham Police Department. This is Detectives Doug Woods, Jim Daniels, and Jack Douglas. May we speak to you in private?"

Maya shook her head in agreement as Sally left, closing the glass door behind her. Maya thought to herself, private? This entire room was surrounded by glass. There was not much privacy here.

"Please sit," Maya offered, sitting at the head of the table, pulling her skirt down as she sat. The men took their seat around the table.

"We want to talk to you about your husband and the Singh family, more specifically, Mark Singh," Chief Insp. Pierce continued, seemingly unaware of Maya's tension.

"What about my husband?" she asked, wondering what they have done now.

"We have to let you know that we had your private phone line tapped," he continued. "Your boss knows about this as we had to provide her with a wiretap order."

Maya's mouth was dry. She looked up at him in disbelief.

"We know that you are not involved in the illegal activities of the Singh family, and we know that you are trying to leave the home, and your husband," Insp. Pierce continued, now noticing Maya's growing tension and nervousness.

"Does my boss know of what they do?" Maya asked nervously.

"No, but she suspects that something is happening that may cause you some worry and apprehension," Insp. Pierce assured her.

"You have her full support, should you need it," he continued.

"Thanks," Maya replied lamely, looking around to see if Lori, her boss, was anywhere nearby.

"Listen, we know that you are planning on leaving, we know you want out soon, and we can help you do that," Insp. Pierce said encouragingly.

"I am definitely not leaving without my children," Maya pronounced.

"We know," Dt. Doug Woods spoke for the first time. "We will help you do that too."

"Why, why do you want to help me? What is in it for you?" Maya retorted.

"Well, we have been investigating the Singh family for some time now, several months, in fact."

"Can police listen to phone conversations on your landline?" Maya asked, still in disbelief of what is happening.

"Yes, we can listen in under certain conditions," Insp. Pierce replied. "The wiretaps have helped gather supportive evidence against the Singh's, who are suspected of highly criminal activity."

"Since it is a severe invasion of privacy, though, it comes with strict procedures for law enforcement. Before we could eavesdrop on your conversations, we had to obtain something called a wiretap order," Insp. Piece continued. "Since wiretapping is extremely intrusive, a wiretap order is a bit more complicated to obtain than a warrant. Our department had to prove probable cause for the judge to believe that that listening to the conversations would help us investigate these serious illegal activities that your family is conducting."

Maya was just staring at him, trying to wrap her head around what is happening. Will they arrest her? She didn't do anything wrong. Yes, she did not report the illegal activities to the police, but she had no part in it.

Insp. Pierce continued, sensing her tension and downcast attitude.

"There is evidence of illegal alien smuggling, terrorism, money laundering, weapons and drug trafficking."

Insp. Pierce was looking at Maya. She was pale. She felt sick, queasy. Maya knew of the dozens of people coming from Guyana every week. She knew of the passport machine and the fake passports, the drugs, weapons, and money laundering.

What the hell am I living in? she thought in horror. Everything flashed before her. The rapes, the horrid behaviors of Mark and Jason. The extorsion of so many people, the guns they were always carrying around. The early morning escapades, the 'meetings' in the basement.

"We need more evidence, and we need your help with that," Dt. Doug Woods brought her back to the present.

"How, how could I help? I... I don't know much," she stammered. Maya grabbed a glass of water and gulped it down in a hurry.

"We do not know their names; we cannot make sense of who they are referring to. We need someone to connect the dots," Insp. Pierce offered.

"Oh, you mean like their nicknames," Maya inquired. "Guyanese people often have more than one name."

She thought, *of course, we have a 'book' name, 'call' name, 'nickname' and a 'false' name.* But she didn't say that to the strict-looking chief and detectives. She didn't think they would understand.

"Yes, nicknames, can you help us associate the names with each person?" Doug Wood asked.

"Yes, I can do that if you will get my children and me away from there first," Maya said hopefully.

"We can do that, but we need to ensure we have a solid case, with solid evidence."

"Are you able to continue living there while helping us to gather evidence?"

"It is not going to be easy," one of the other detectives said. Maya did not recall his name.

"I may know enough about the alien smuggling, but I know nothing of the other stuff," Maya explained.

"We just need your help with the names," he replied. "Don't worry. It is our job to gather the evidence before we can proceed with search warrants and arrests."

"We are hoping to gather all evidence to have arrests and warrants before Christmas," he continued.

"That is two months away!" Maya exclaimed, "I thought we are doing this right away." She thought, this is finally going to happen. The police will protect her now.

"These things take time. Right now, we have some of our detectives working with the local Police in Guyana," Insp. Pierce explained. "Until he returns with the evidence he gathered in Guyana, we cannot proceed."

"In Guyana?" Maya asked, puzzled.

"Yes, we have reason to believe that the key player and the head of the organization is living in Guyana."

"What is his name?" Maya asked. "Maybe I know this person."

"Have you heard of Lance Baksh?"

"No, I have not heard of him," Maya responded.

"What about Scarface?" he asked.

"I've heard that name mentioned a lot. It didn't make sense to me at the time, I thought they were talking about the movie."

"He calls himself Scarface. He is the leader of the backtracking organization. He is charging a reported US$10,000 per client," Insp. Pierce explained.

"They are allegedly aided by immigration and airport personnel in Guyana. They are smuggling about ten clients a week to the United States and Canada," he continued. "It is reported that things don't usually go too well for those who tried to flee this 'Scarface.'"

Maya watched Insp. Pierce in shock and utter disbelief. She swallowed hard. She felt cold. This is not a nightmare; this is not a horrible gangster movie. This is reality. This is HER reality. She is a witness to these horrific allegations.

All of this could not happen to one person. Maya tried to stand up, and her knees buckled. Insp. Pierce grabbed her arms to steady her. She felt faint. Her memory flashed back to that young lad.

"I saw it," she whispered.

"What did you say?" Insp. Pierce asked.

"I saw it, I saw what happened to one young man."

"Can you describe this young man?"

"No, his face was covered in blood. I didn't see him that well. I saw the two men beating him," Maya said nervously.

"We have information that Scarface had abducted a young man's mother and sister after this young man failed to cough up the full payment for his 'backtrack' fee."

Maya was in disbelief. Was she a witness to an abduction? Extortion? Murder?

"Mrs. Singh, we do not want to upset you further. We will take leave now but will be in touch shortly. Going forward, we will call you here at work as well," Insp. Pierce explained.

"Detective Woods will stay in touch with you. From what we can interpret from your conversations with your lawyer, we believe it is best if we call you or meet right here at your workplace," Insp. Pierce explained. "Your boss is very understanding and cooperative and has given us the OK to do so."

"We have taken up far too much of your time," Dt. Woods got up as well. "We will be in touch shortly, stay safe, keep a low profile. I will call you on Wednesday."

"Thank you all," Maya offered, not knowing what else to say.

She went back to her office. She felt drained, baffled. Lori came over.

"Don't despair, everything will work itself out," she said reassuringly. "Maya, I want you to know that I suspected a long time ago that you were having problems at home, but I did not want to intrude. It's not normal to have anxiety attacks so often."

Maya shook her head in agreement. Looking back, she knew that Lori must have known something was not right. She was thankful that Lori never pressured her about it.

"You are a valued employee, and you are very good at your job. We don't want to lose you," Lori continued. "But I really think you need to take some personal time off."

"No, I can't. If I do, my family will get suspicious. I need to be here," Maya said. Lori agreed, and they both went back to work.

That evening, Maya was highly uncomfortable at dinner. She wondered if they knew.

Chapter Eight

Aliens & Smugglers

Maya continued work and got weekly calls from Dt. Doug Woods. She helped him with the names, and he updated her with the progress they were making.

They worked closely with the R.C.M.P. Immigration Department, the Drug Enforcement Unit, and the chief of Police in Guyana, who so happened to be Maya's uncle. They seemed to be taking far too long with their investigation, and Maya wondered how long she could continue pretending that everything was normal at home. Mark and Roselle's travel to Guyana and the U.S. seemed to be getting more frequent, and there were far too many 'clients' staying at the house now. Maya wished she could take the children and run away.

The house was so full that there was nowhere for privacy. She spent many evenings at the nearby park with the children until dusk, coming home just in time for the children to have a bath, read bedtime stories, and then get tucked in bed. After the children were asleep, Maya would continue eavesdropping on the activities in the basement. She came to find out that the operation now involved blank passports and Canadian passport seals.

It seemed that Mark and Roselle were building a house in Guyana in the prestigious neighborhood of Prasad Nagar. Unknown to the Singhs, the Police continued wiretapping the phones at home and at all Mark's sisters' homes as well. On one of their weekly calls, Insp. Pierce informed Maya that the Police were also tapping the phones of Mark's associates in Guyana.

The evidence seemed to indicate that Mark had a counterpart in Guyana, the Guyanese ringleader. The R.C.M.P. operatives in Guyana were listening to conversations between this ringleader and several of Mark's associates in Guyana.

As the Durham Police and the R.C.M.P. continued their investigation, Maya's anxiety increased by the day. She desperately needed a break to get out of the house and have a moment without fear.

That day came in early September. The weather was starting to cool down. Kyle was heading back to school, and it was a bit daunting for Maya. She could not believe he was already four years old.

It was a long week, Maya looked forward to the weekend. It was her sister, Nadia's birthday and her parents had planned a birthday party at their place, with her sisters and their families. She did not bring the kids. It was one of those rare times that she and Jason went out without the children. Surprisingly, Jason agreed to come with her.

Maya was back down to size zero from her pregnancy with Ryder.

She wore a black off-shoulder crop top over leggings, a black leather jacket with shoulder pads and slouched socks. Her hair was big and curly, typical style for the 80's. Everyone complimented how great she looked. For once, she felt good, and she was very happy to be with her family.

Maya and her sisters had a few glasses of wine. Maya was not a drinker, and two glasses of wine was more than enough for her, but she had a few more with the encouragement of her sisters and brothers-in-law. She got a lot more drunk than she expected, whereas Jason only had one drink before taking her home.

The next thing she remembered was lying on their bed, with him next to her. None of this was distressing, she was in a good mood as far as she was concerned. Jason started to kiss her, she reciprocated, but she could feel that he wanted more after a few minutes. She told him that she didn't feel like having sex and just wanted to sleep.

"I had a lot to drink," she said sleepily.

Sleep quickly got the better of her, and Maya fell asleep, fully clothed. When she awoke the next day, she was naked from the waist down. She recalls brief flashes of opening her eyes and seeing him on top of her. She was vaguely aware of her body being moved, but she was too drunk to respond. She was conscious of what was happening in the innermost part, but the rest of her brain was just blank.

Her first thought was how embarrassed she was at being so drunk the night before. She felt slightly sore between her legs, and when she checked, she could tell there was semen on the inside of her legs and a little blood on the bedsheets.

When Jason woke up, she asked him if they had sex, and he casually said yes.

"I only realized halfway through that you were asleep, so I quickly finished and went to sleep myself." He seemed so calm and a matter of fact about it. As if her saying no, refusing, did not matter.

As the days went on, Maya began to feel uneasy about what happened. She felt disrespected. Increasingly, whenever she chose not to have sex with him, he would pester her repeatedly until she gave in. It genuinely felt easier just to let him get on with it than contest it, because he would not let her sleep or get on with her work until he got what he wanted.

And then, in early November, came that fateful day. Maya had worked late and did not get home until after 10:00 pm. When she got home, she was disgusted to find that the sink was filled with dishes. Maya dropped her purse and keys on the table and started cleaning up. Tired, angry, and upset at the fact that there were so many people living in the house, and yet they expected her to clean up after them, even though she had called home to say she had to work late. As she was washing the dishes, Jason entered the kitchen.

"Are you coming up soon?" he asked.

"I have to finish the dishes," she replied, not looking up from the sink full of soapy dishes.

Jason came over to her and began kissing her roughly.

"Stop, I need to finish this, and I am tired," she tried to push him away, but he carried on until she lost her temper and had to push him hard again.

He laughed in her face, pulled her body towards the floor, her ribs slammed to the ground. He pushed her up against the wall and kicked her.

As she lay on her back, Jason then stopped on her chest several times. Maya gasped for air. He grabbed her by the hair and yanked her up on the kitchen table. He then flung her dress up, and raped her, forcefully raped her right there in the kitchen. Maya was terrified, and she kept telling him to stop. Jason ignored her pleas. With the look on his face, the satisfaction, he knew exactly what he was doing. Maya stopped resisting, she just lay there, unresponsive, and waited for it to end, hoping no one heard anything.

At that moment, everything clicked into place. Maya had been sexually abused in her own home, by her husband, and before by his brother. This was the breaking point. It had taken her a long time, but this was finally the last straw.

Maya kept repeating this over in her head, again and again. It finally dawned on her precisely what Jason was doing to her. How did she let this happen to her all these years? It will never end.

How long will the police take? There was no way she could survive in this house anymore, no way she could continue to be sexually abused, emotionally abused, and physically abuse. She went to bed quietly that night. The next day was a holiday, but she got dressed and went to work. Jason asked why she was going to work on a holiday, and she claimed it was because the project they were working on still needed modifying, even though they stayed late the night before. This was true, and the rest of the staff was going in to finish the project. Maya's part of the job was done at this point, but she didn't care.

"I'll drop you," Jason offered.

"Why? I can drive."

"Ivan asked to borrow your car, and I said it was okay since today is a holiday and I thought you were going to be home."

Maya was too exhausted and tired of all the lies.

"Fine."

They drove to Maya's workplace in silence. The traffic was light on the Don Valley Parkway. One look at Maya and Lori knew something was wrong. They went to the boardroom, and Maya poured her heart out to Lori, who already knew that Maya's home life was troubled.

"I have to leave, Lori, I can't stay there, I can't let my children live like this," Maya said sadly.

"I know, let's start making a plan, I am not letting you go back there," Lori said firmly.

Maya looked out the window as they spoke, preoccupied with her thoughts, when she realized that Jason's jeep was parked under the tree, right outside the building entrance. Lori saw Maya's face crumble.

"How am I getting out if here now, he is watching me," Maya was in hysterics. "If he knows that I am leaving, he will go and take the kids away."

"I think you need to call Insp. Pierce," Lori encouraged. Maya nodded and reached for her purse to get the number.

Insp. Pierce answered right away.

"I need out now," Maya exclaimed. "I need your help, I cannot wait for this investigation, I need out now."

"What happened," Insp. Tom Pierce immediately knew Maya was in distress.

"I don't want to make a report, I just want to get my children out of there," Maya was afraid if she reported that Jason beat and raped her, she would lose her children.

She thought, *maybe I deserved it. I should let him have sex with me, I am his wife after all, it is his right.* She was quiet for a moment.

Insp. Pierce, sensing her hesitation, urged, "Tell me what happened."

Maya looked at Lori, unable to speak. Lori took the phone.

"Inspector, this is Lori. Maya was beaten and raped last night. You need to get her out of there."

"No, no, don't tell him that," Maya pleaded with Lori.

Lori looked at her in shock, realizing that this poor woman is so afraid.

Insp. Tom Pierce talked to Lori, "Can she get to the station? She needs to make a report."

"No, her husband is outside our office building. He dropped her off this morning and has been waiting outside since then. As you know, this is not a regular day, and we do not even have daytime security," Lori explained.

"If we come for her, he will be suspicious. Can someone bring her?" Tom asked.

"No, if any of us leaves with her, there is no way he won't see us. All cars are parked out front today. The back lots are closed on holidays."

"We have to get her to the station," Insp. Tom Pierce said as he thought of other ways.

"Wait, I know away!" Lori exclaimed.

"How?" Insp. Tom Pierce and Maya both asked at the same time.

"The Armoured Truck!" Lori said excitedly. "We have an armored truck that goes to the bank every day, it is parked underground, and there is an exit that comes out on the next street."

Lori's excitement was growing, she felt like a cop or even a private detective. "That jackass won't know a thing."

"That's great, Lori. I will call the R.C.M.P. right away to see about a search warrant. I will meet you at the station." Insp. Pierce hung up.

Lori's plan went off without a hitch. After locating a driver for the truck, Maya snuck out through the underground garage. The vehicle exited north of the building and turned east towards the D.V.P.

Maya was at the police station in less than 20 minutes. Insp. Pierce was waiting eagerly at the back of the building and Maya was hustled into the station. Ironically, the station was at the intersection of where they lived, and Maya's thoughts went back to when it was being built. She always wondered how Mark, Jason, and the rest of their gang were not afraid of being caught with the police right there in their neighborhood. Maya remembered thinking, 'they are making a brand-new police station just for the Singhs." She used to play the song, *bad boys, bad boys, what you were going to do when they come for you*, on repeat and she used to hope they would get the hint. She smiled to herself warily, watching Insp. Pierce's broad shoulders ahead of her.

Insp. Tom Pierce walked ahead, Maya feeling like a dwarf behind him, her heels clicking noisily in the quiet hallway.

They entered a bright room with paneled glass windows around the entire room.

Insp. Rahul Khan, R.C.M.P. Immigration Division, introduced himself in a very authoritative voice.

He looked brown like Maya, but he had no Caribbean or Indian accent, so she could not tell where he was from. Indeed, he was not born in Canada. Even in her current misfortunate situation, Maya noticed that he was extremely attractive — tall, with black curly hair. He stood over six feet tall with a very muscular body. He smiled reassuringly. That dimpled smile made her heart skip a beat and made her smile even when she was hurting.

"I am here on the request of the Chief of Police, Insp. Tom Pierce," he said firmly. "As you are aware, they have been investigating your husband and his family. I am aware that you have been cooperating with the detectives on their investigation."

Maya was not really in the mood for this conversation, all she could think about is that if Jason finds out she is not at work, he will take the kids away. She just needed to get her kids.

"Can we do this later?" she asked, hopefully.

"We cannot help you if you do not help us," Insp. Rahul Khan said flatly.

Maya did not want to move from the window, where she had a clear view of the street. Jason would have to pass the police station to get home.

"Can we sit right here where I can see the street? Jason will be heading home when he realizes he did not see me leave work. I am afraid he will take the kids and I won't see them again," she voiced her fears to Insp. Rahul Khan.

"Wait here," he said and left, sliding the glass door behind him. Within a few minutes, he was back.

"Do not worry, one off our female officers is on her way. She will wait at the end of the street until she sees his car," Insp. Rahul Khan assured Maya.

"When he drives up the driveway, she will arrest him there for rape and assault, so that he will not be able to take the kids."

"We need to wait for a search warrant and since it is a holiday, we cannot get a hold of a judge," Dt. Wood said. Maya did not even see him enter the room; her focus was on the street. The streetlights had turned on, and it was beginning to get dark. Maya was afraid that she would not see if Jason went past the police station.

"I called a friend of mine who is a judge in this town. We are waiting for her to sign the search warrant, as soon as we get that we are going in," Insp. Rahul Khan explained.

"Don't worry, Mr. Singh cannot get your kids, the charges are too serious," he continued. "Come, let's go upstairs, it is much more comfortable and private."

Maya suddenly realized that this was the reporting area, and people were coming and going most evenings.

She followed Insp. Rahul Khan and Dt. Pierce, with Dt. Woods slightly behind her. They walked through security doors into an elevator and up to the second floor. Maya realized how suddenly uncomfortable she was. Everyone was hurrying around with files and papers in their hands. The policemen and women were all in uniform. They were all looking at her as they walked by. Some with sympathy and some interest in their eyes. Maya thought to herself, *this must be a big case and they must have been following me, as they seem to recognize me.*

There was no number on the elevator, just a scanner that responded to Insp. Pierce's touch. They emerged into a long, semi-circular, glass-paneled corridor that seemed to match the rest of the building. People were moving about here as well, but no one spoke or looked up. There were also fewer people in uniform here.

Insp. Rahul Khan shut the door behind them, the click of the latch easily sliding over an internal bolt.

"Mrs. Singh, we will talk about what happened today but also, I would like to talk about what you know about the illegal activities of your family," Insp. Rahul Khan was very professional in his approach.

"Please call me Maya," she said quickly, detesting the fact that her last name associated her with that family.

"Sure, Maya," Insp. Rahul Khan smiled, as if hearing her thoughts. "Look, I understand that you do not want to talk about this now and that you are worried about your children. However, I must warn you that you are in a dangerous situation. When you leave your house tonight, you cannot go to your parents or any of your family as you will be putting them in danger as well."

"What!! Where would I go then?" she asked in disbelief.

"We have made arrangements for you to go to a shelter until everything is sorted out, but first we will take you home to get your children as we conduct our search warrants and arrests," Dt. Doug Woods reassured her.

"Do you know where they keep the passports, the guns, the seals and machines?" Insp. Rahul Khan asked.

Maya nodded. She had seen the passport machine behind the thick red velvet curtains in Kayla's bedroom. She had seen boxes of bullets, guns, seals, money, and things she did not understand, all in the basement.

She recalled opening Kyle's closet doors once, and boxes of bullets fell on her head. She quietly packed it back on the shelf, knowing that it would be evidence one day.

Chapter Nine

Arresting Development

The plan was to wait for the search warrant. The idea was for the Singhs not to get away or hide any of the equipment. The police were clearly not ready. Maya's situation and the need to move things faster than anticipated seem to hinder this plan.

Maya's urgency to get the kids meant that the investigation was now in jeopardy. For this reason, they wanted to arrested Jason for assault and domestic abuse to stall until the warrant was ready. Insp. Rahul walked back from the water cooler and placed a glass of water in front of Maya.

"Here, drink this," he offered. "Maya, we would like to share some information with you. The detective here tells me that they have met with you and have been in touch with you for several weeks now."

"Yes," Maya gulped down the water quickly, not realizing how thirsty she was.

"We know you are not involved in the illegal activities of your husband and his family," Insp. Rahul Khan said. "This has now become a federal case and is being handed over to the R.C.M.P. for further investigation."

"Why?" Maya asked, puzzled. Insp. Pierce or Dt. Doug Woods did not mention this to her before.

"Since there is illegal alien smuggling between three or more countries, as well as other illegal activities too numerous to mention, this investigation is being handed it over to the R.C.M.P.," Insp. Rahul Khan explained.

Maya nodded.

"Detective Insp. Pierce will continue to assist with the investigation, but from here on out, I will be your main point of contact."

"We will be taking you the Denise Shelter as soon as we get your children," he continued. "Maya, you and your children will have to remain there until this investigation is over."

"I will come visit you a couple of times a week, but you will not be able to see anyone or speak about this investigation to anyone. That includes your own family. Do you understand the seriousness and the confidentiality of this case?"

Maya shook her head.

"Yes, I understand. When are we going to get the kids?" she asked, still worried that the family would move the kids before they get there.

"As soon as we have the signed warrant," he assured her.

The search warrant was taking longer due to the holiday. The wait at the police station was terribly slow as the R.C.M.P. team and the police detectives reviewed data on the target area both here in Canada and the international illegal alien smuggling groups between Guyana, the U.S., and Canada. They were doing all this as everyone quietly waited for the search warrant.

While their data said that the group used the border rivers to move the illegal aliens, Maya knew otherwise. She knew how they were being smuggled through and where they were headed. Maya pushed the thoughts out of her head as she tried to understand what was happening with her children. She was doing this only for them. Only to save them from this miserable, unlawful, and insensible family.

She thought of Kyle, who often asked her, "Why does daddy make you sad, mommy?"

There is no way that this is a healthy way for the children to be raised and seeing their parents fighting all the time. Maya's main fear was that her kids would grow up and have the same temperament as their father. This was beyond a toxic relationship.

"Good news, Maya, Detective Pat Lacy got your husband," Insp. Rahul Khan strode back in smiling.

"He is in custody right below us on the basement level. He will be spending the night here for sure," he added.

Dt. Pat Lacy stood a mere five foot two, like Maya, but seemed more petite in her loose-fitting clothes. She wore her blond hair in a noticeably short military-style turf on top and buzz at the sides. Her eyes were a bright blue, but their intensity made them seem turquoise.

"I got him," she announced, beaming in satisfaction. "And he did not go down lightly."

Fueled with rage, Dt. Pat Lacy had left the station as soon as Insp. Rahul Khan told her what had happened to Maya last night. They had just arrived at the house as Jason pulled up on the driveway.

He must have seen the police cruiser behind him. He sped down the tree-lined street and quickly pulled up onto the driveway. The driver-side door flew open, and Jason emerged in a T-shirt, black jeans, and running shoes. He sprinted away from the car and ran towards the hedges at the side of the house.

Dt. Lacy jumped out of the police cruiser and ran after him.

"Police, stop right there," she yelled.

Jason continued running along the side of the hedges, slightly hidden by the bushes.

I could pull my gun and fire at this guy, she thought. But Jason appeared empty-handed, which meant shooting an unarmed man, and a moving target at that, may not work. She was not sure she could hit anyway. In the meantime, Jason had reached the forested area at the back of the house, just before a clearing by the stream.

Dt. Lacy could not shoot Jason at this range. She paused, her gun up near the side of her face. Jason probably knew this area well enough to elude them. She was closing the gap, twenty yards, then ten... then five... until she was about 20 feet. She could hear Jason gasping as he ran.

He laughed as Dt. Lacy dropped her gun and grabbed around his waist, the two hit the ground hard. They rolled over the jagged rocks and hard dark clumps. For a moment, Dt. Lacy had him, but Jason squirmed out of her grip. She grabbed him again and pinned him down with her knees on his chest as she picked up her gun again.

"Don't fucking move punk!" she barked and hit him across the face, still holding the gun.

Dt. Warner ran up behind Dt. Lacy, panting and out of breath, pointing his pistol at the suspect though it was evident that Jason could not move. Dt. Warner grabbed him up and handcuffed him.

"Read him his fucking Miranda Rights before I beat the shit out of this jackass," Dt. Lacy snarled as Dt Warner pulled out handcuffs.

"You are under arrest, *"You have the right to remain silent. Anything you say can and will be used against you in a court of law. You have the right to an attorney. If you cannot afford an attorney, one will be provided for you. Do you understand the rights I have just read to you?*

"Yes," Jason responded.

They shoved him down the pathway roughly and were about to push him into the cruiser when the front door of the house open and Sal stood there in shock.

"Move the kids," Jason shouted to Sal.

"You move those kids, and you are in big fucking trouble," Dt. Lacy yelled at Sal. "Don't even think about it. Your son is arrested for rape and assault. You may want to call a lawyer."

They drove off.

Back at the station, Maya was still anxiously waiting. Insp. Rahul Khan and Insp. Pierce were talking about search warrants. Apparently, they did not have enough evidence to get warrants for all the Singhs' homes, and due to the holiday, they were very limited in their request, they were only granted a search warrant to search Maya and Jason's home. Maya didn't care, she just wanted her children.

Finally, Dt. Doug Woods came in through the door, waving some papers in the air. "We got it," he shouted.

"Let's go," Insp. Rahul Khan ordered.

The Special Weapons and Tactic (S.W.A.T.) unit were already geared up in bullet proof vests, guns, and batons, just waiting for that order. They got to their feet, hustling out the door. The team of officers of about 30 or so, all dressed in black, with the word S.W.A.T. written across the back of their jackets, pulled up to the driveway, covering the lawn and the sides of the house. At the time, Maya did not know what S.W.A.T meant. She felt like she was part of a movie, like none of this was real.

She was sure that there were over 25 cars. The team jumped out of the vehicles, bright lights from the cars lighting up the house. There were no sirens.... just lights. The team quietly moved towards the house, their rifles all aiming towards the doors and windows.

Dt. Lacy pulled Maya aside.

"You stay right behind me, do not be afraid, do not be intimidated. Do not look at anyone. I will be with you throughout this," Dt. Lacy said reassuringly. "Grab what you want for the children, and I will help you to get the children."

Maya felt like her knees were about to give out under her. Her nerves were shot. She was petrified. As they entered the house, Mark was standing apart from the others at the doorway. Two more men emerged from the basement. Dt. Lacy immediately walked before Maya and asked where the kids were.

Mark pointed upstairs but did not say anything. His face stone cold, he did not even flinch as

Insp. Pierce moved forward and placed handcuffs on him and read him his rights.

"Spread out," Insp. Rahul Khan ordered. The team moved around to different parts of the house in groups as Maya followed Lacy up the stairs, feeling like a stranger in her own home.

As Maya nervously got the kids up, she felt so contrite. They were so confused. Kyle was sleeping in Kayla's room, who just stood there in shock. Maya looked at her apologetically. She shook her head as if to tell Maya, 'It's okay, I understand."

"Mom what is happening?" asked Kyle rubbing his eyes.

"Mom is taking you to a safe place," Maya assured him.

"Why are we not safe here, mom?" he asked, always filled with so many questions.

"Because mommy is not safe here. And mommy must take you with her," Maya said, hugging him.

Dt. Pat Lacy was right behind Maya. Insp. Rahul Khan came to the door.

"Maya, where is the passport stuff?" he asked gently.

Maya pointed to the red velvet curtains in Kayla's bedroom.

Dt. Woods reached over and picked up a black square suitcase-like box.

"Did you get some clothes for the children?" Dt. Lacy asked.

"No, it's okay." Maya did not want anything from this house. This blood money. She wanted out, and she didn't want to take anything with her.

Maya stepped into the upstairs hallway, holding Ryder in her arms, Kyle held on to her skirt, and Dt. Lacy had Melena in her arms. Maya feared leaving. The household was tense. As soon as Jason got arrested, they knew something was coming. They must have already packed ammo, ready to defend themselves. Maya was scared for her parents, for her sisters, her family. She was afraid for herself.

Chapter Ten

Breaking Bad

The search continued, but Dt. Lacy hustled Maya and the children into a police car. Sal was in the foyer.

"Why do you have to take the children?" he asked. "We can work this out. You do not have to remove them from their home. This is their home."

Dt. Lacy looked at him with her piercing eyes. "Did I not tell you to stay out of this?"

"We are removing her from an unsafe and unhealthy environment and her children are going with her. Her husband can work this out in Family Court." Her bright blue eyes were piercing into his.

"What the team is here for has nothing to do with the domestic violence she and her children have been exposed. This is a different matter sir," she continued. Sal backed away. Kayla handed something to Maya.

"Here, take this, it will protect you and the children" she said kindly.

It was a small book of the "Hanuman Chalisa,' one of a few that Maya used to put under the children's pillow for protection. She always felt uneasy in this house, like a dark shadow was looming over them. Reciting the 'Hanuman Chalisa' always made her feel calm and gave her inner peace.

Insp. Rahul Khan was giving instructions to the SWAT team but came up to the car as Maya arrived.

"Do not worry, you are in good hands," he assured Maya. "We will meet you out there shortly, Detective Pierce and I."

Maya clung to the children in the back of the car as they drove away in silence. Both girls were sleepy, but Kyle was wide awake, looking out the window. Maya so desperately wanted to hold him to her chest and comfort him. He seemed so mature already and was ready to help Maya with Ryder. As they got to the shelter, some exceedingly kind women were waiting for them, and they were ushered in quickly.

The only things Maya had with her were the children's teddy bears, her purse, and what they were wearing. Noticing that, the shelter director comforted her, saying they had a room waiting.

It was about 2:00 AM in the morning by now. Dt. Lacy hugged Maya and assured her that she was doing the right thing and that she is a strong woman. She left just as quickly, and Maya didn't even get the chance to thank her for all that she had done.

The shelter director took them up to two flights of stairs into a room that was overlooking a small, dimly lit garden. This was going to be their new home for the next few months. The ladies helped Maya tuck the children into bed and asked if she needed anything. Maya realized that she had not eaten anything all day except for a cup of tea at the police station. She gently asked Kyle if he was hungry, but he nodded no. Maya kissed him goodnight and tucked the small book of the 'Hanuman Chalisa' under his pillow. She immediately fell onto the pillow beside him, exhausted. Her mind was reeling, her heart racing, images of everything she had been through were flashing through her head.

She exhaled. *Is it finally over? Can I finally breathe?*

Was she finally freeing from this relationship filled with abuse, mistrust, anger, and so much sadness?

In the back of her mind she thought, *I was stupid to have been with this person. Nobody else is going to want me after this relationship.*

She shook her head, determined not to put herself down anymore.

In the months that followed, Maya learned so much about abuse and domestic violence. She could not believe how many women were in similar situations, experiencing domestic violence and abuse from their partners, husbands, and even their fathers and mothers.

There was one girl whose head was shaved bald. The girl appeared to Maya to be way too young to be here. In one of their group sessions, she broke down in tears and told the group that her stepfather was sexually abusing her. When she told her mother, her mother did not believe her, and together they both shaved her head. She was kept locked away for many years until one day, she was finally able to break free.

There was another, named Allegra, a mother of three children just like Maya. She was beautiful and elegant with dark black hair down to her waist. She seems to be very disturbed, always on guard. Eventually, in a group session, she shared that her husband is in the Italian Mafia. She did not speak of many things, and she, just like Maya, was also getting private counseling. Some women were allowed to leave and go to work, but Maya and Allegra, they were not even allowed to go out the front of the building. They had to remain indoors and were only allowed to go into the back garden. It was heavily gated with extremely high hedges all around. Allegra and Maya became close friends in the months to follow, and their children would often play with each other in the garden. They never shared their stories with each other. They both were not allowed to go anywhere or even to see their family or friends.

One day Maya was in a group therapy session, and she was told that she got a phone call. It was puzzling because the only two people that call her are her mother on Sundays and her lawyer on Tuesdays. Today was Wednesday. She nervously answered the phone. To her utmost shock, it was Jason.

"Hi, how are the kids?" he asked. Maya just stood there in disbelief, she could not even answer.

"How did you find me?" she asked nervously.

"You know that is extremely easy. I just got my friend to call and say that she is being abused, and they told her that she can go to the new shelter," he said mockingly. "You know there is only one shelter in Durham."

Maya quickly hung up the phone and told the counsellor what happened, who assured her that they could not get her in here. There is a triple lock door, and she is safe here. They promise to screen all calls in the future.

No one was allowed to visit Maya, no one that is, except for Insp. Rahul Khan. He called once a week in the beginning and then three times a week. He told Maya that Jason got out on bail but not to worry; he cannot harm her at the shelter.

Insp. Rahul Khan wanted information about the aliases of each person in the Singh family. As with the norm of Guyanese immigrants, they all have several nicknames and aliases. This confused the investigation and the wiretapping immensely. They could not understand which name or nickname belonged to what person, as they all had more than one or two names. Insp. Rahul Khan claims that this is the only assistance he needed from Maya to build a "name tree" for each person with aliases and relate to each other.

Maya did not want to talk about this; she wants to put it behind her. She was consumed with hate and anger.

The RCMP offered her a witness protection program, but she refused. She was determined that she did not want to run from these monsters.

Insp. Rahul Khan shared that RCMP and the local police detectives were working closely with the U.S. and Canadian border agency in the investigation. Mark and his associates were powerfully involved in a larger ring of alien smuggling, weapons, drugs, passport forging. It seemed that Mark was not the kingpin after all.

The Kingpin lived in Guyana, someone named Baksh, internationally known by law enforcement agencies for trafficking illegal aliens, drug, weapons, and so much more. Mark, Jason, and their associates were merely pawns in a giant scheme.

Insp. Rahul Khan shared the U.S. Embassy confirmed that they knew of Baksh's escapades and had denied his application for a U.S. immigrant visa. As a result, he was ineligible for an immigrant visa under laws that prohibited anyone who had "wrongly aided, abetted anyone to enter the U.S. illegally."

Nevertheless, Insp. Rahul Khan claimed that Baksh had managed to slip into the US on several occasions, and they are on the hunt for him in Queens, New York. In his application for a US visa, Baksh had informed the US Embassy that he owned several properties in the US and estimated his assets at US$400,000.00 at the time. Insp. Rahul Khan shared that they were interrogating Mark. They would offer him a plea deal for his willingness to testify against Baksh on one condition that he be deported to Guyana and never return to Canada.

Maya asked about Jason. Will he be deported too? Insp. Rahul Khan said they did not have enough evidence for that. Unfortunately, there was no evidence to even charge him for assault or rape, as Maya was never given a rape kit test. A rape kit to gather and preserve physical evidence following an allegation of the assault. She was not even taken to the hospital or seen a doctor. There was no evidence collected from Maya that can aid the criminal rape investigation to have a credible case for sexual assault investigations.

In their haste to catch Mark Singh, they completely neglected to investigate Maya's assault. What an emotional blow for Maya. She was trembling. Realizing that both the local police and the RCMP's interest in the investigation was far more important to them than what happened to Maya. This was something that filled her with rage and stayed with her for a very long time.

Chapter Eleven

Guns and Roses

On a dark wintery day in January, Insp. Rahul Khan called the shelter to let them know he was making an unexpected visit to see Maya. As Maya came into the small boardroom, he sat with his hands on the table, his fingers crisscrossed over a manilla file folder. He smiled weakly. Insp. Rahul Khan's striking appearance and engaging personality had already won a firm place in Maya's heart. His kindness towards her and the children was all that was holding her together, and his visits were all she had looked forward to for months now.

On this day, his curly hair was falling over his forehead as if he desperately needed a haircut.

"I have some good news and I have some bad news," he said, his weak smile was gone.

"Bad news first," Maya replied, sitting down in front of him. This was their usual setup.

"Okay, here goes," he said. "Read this."

He handed her what looked like a report from the manilla folder.

> *Early Tuesday afternoon, someone put a bullet into the back of Baksh's head as he was watching TV with a few friends in the living room of his posh, stylish home in the exclusive part of Georgetown, Guyana.*
>
> *Six armed men suddenly entered through the backdoor. First, the men ordered the frightened occupants to lie on the floor. Then, warning them to remain silent, the gunmen turned the television up to its highest volume. While three of the men stayed with the group, Baksh was pushed into the back bedroom. Minutes later, the muffled sound of a gunshot was heard. The men exited the room, fleeing via the back door. His friends found Baksh lying face down, motionless. He had been shot in the back of the neck.*
>
> *The Local police confirmed that a search of the slain Baksh's home unearthed several blank US passports and forged passport seals, fentanyl, cocaine, suspected hydromorphone pills, digital scales, US, and Canadian cash, prohibited weapons, rifles, body armor, marijuana. Cocaine and other prohibited drugs.*
>
> *What had been a months-long investigation' has now abruptly come to a sudden halt. The death of Baksh has ended one of the largest backtracking rings in the US and Canada as well as Guyana.*

Maya looked up at Insp. Rahul Khan in shock.

"Who shot him?" she asked.

"It is still under investigation, but less than a week after Baksh's death, police rounded up several suspects. Among them was a 28-year-old individual, Daniel Simpson. You may know him as 'Pookie,'" Insp. Rahul Khan stated.

"Oh my god," Maya gasped. "He was my employee at the phone company. He was Jason's friend, and he asked for a favour as he had family back home to support."

"Well, although you hired him, the intention was for him to keep an eye on you," he said gravely.

"Jesus Christ! I hired a murderer!" Maya exclaimed, jumping up from the table.

"An alleged murderer," Insp. Rahul Khan corrected.

"Where is Mark?" she asked, standing over Insp. Rahul Khan, her mind racing.

"He was deported about two weeks ago," he replied.

"And this is not a coincidence that Baksh got killed two weeks after Mark went back to Guyana? Was Baksh the victim of a tainted backtrack deal?" she questioned.

"We are considering all scenarios, and nothing is off the table," Insp. Rahul Khan assured. "I am going to Guyana; I am leaving tonight."

"Okay, what is the good news" Maya asked, sitting back down.

"You can now move on with your life, you can leave this place. You can return to work," Insp. Rahul Khan encouraged. "Kyle can go to school, and you can try to find some normalcy. The court will probably grant you full custody, but I wouldn't be surprised if Jason fights you on that."

"Court?" Maya asked, puzzled. "I thought you helped me to get the kids, why do I need to go to court?"

"You must understand that this is a family court matter in which we have no jurisdiction. You still need to obtain a court order for custody," he advised.

"I didn't know that! I should have been told this," Maya argued. "I was under the assumption that for offering my assistance, you helped me get the kids."

"We helped you to remove them, it is now your responsibility to keep them in your care," he said softly. "I do not believe this will be difficult as they were removed from a home that had them in extreme risks, threatening their wellbeing."

Maya shook her head in disbelief.

"Don't worry, I will always be here for you. I will help you, and you can call me anytime, even when I am in Guyana."

This was not untrue. For many years to come, Maya could reach out to Rahul any time she needed to, even in the middle of the night.

The very next day, Maya started planning for her move. The director assured her that the Government will aid her financially in finding a home and enable her to start the proceedings to obtain full custody of the children. One good thing was that she was able to keep the children in her care throughout the proceedings.

Maya's first decision was to move out of this region. Although she could not move out of Ontario; she could move to a different city and closer to her work. However, Maya never received much help from the government as she had a well-paying job.

Insp. Rahul Khan's prediction of her having full custody was not as on target as he had predicted. For many years, Maya endured two separate and lengthy court battles for the children. In the next few weeks, Insp. Rahul Khan returned to visit her several times at the shelter and had provided an update on his visit to Guyana. The accused, Daniel Simpson, had appeared in the Georgetown Magistrates' Court and was charged with Baksh's murder. Several months after Baksh's execution, the RCMP cracked a massive alien-smuggling ring with links to Guyana, the US, and Canada. Some of the culprits were removed from the Cheddi Jagran International Airport for aiding the 'backtrack' clients who departed Guyana. Others would be arrested in Canada and the US.

After leaving the shelter, Maya found peace in a small apartment in Scarborough. She kept in touch with Lori, and she started to build a new life with Kyle, Melena, and Ryder. Lori was kind enough to let Maya take as long as she needed to sort her life and promised that Maya would have her job back when she was ready to return to work.

Kyle was now in senior kindergarten, and Melena was just starting junior. Maya and Ryder would walk them to school every morning and then back for lunch. Melena's school was only half day. Maya spent the rest of the day doing arts and crafts with the girls until picking Kyle up from school. They would watch TV on a small television that was a loaner from Maya's dad in the evenings. They had one rocking chair and one mattress that they would all sleep on. Life was good, and Jason stayed away as ordered, as the court date for their custody case was not set until January.

What began as simple custody battle for visitation rights eventually dragged on for more than eighteen years as Sal decided that he and Kayla were the best caregivers for the children. Sal fought for control of the children until he died, and Ryder was almost eighteen years old by then.

But we are getting ahead of the story.

By this time, Insp. Rahul Khan was a regular visitor, and the children were getting used to his visits. He would bring news of the investigation, or lack of it at this point. Insp. Rahul Khan was moved to another department after the Singhs case was dissolved and could not offer anything else. He was now undercover for some other high-profile case. After the assassination of Baksh, and with Mark and Roselle's return to Guyana, Maya had no reason to be afraid of Jason or the family. She always knew that it was Mark who led them down a path of aggression, violence, theft, scams, rip-offs, and swindles. He was the leader that spearheaded the destruction of the Singhs. With Mark gone, they would have no choice but to return to everyday life.

The custody battles and dealings with Jason and Sal were on a weekly basis at this point. The unfortunate thing about custody cases is that Maya could not bring up any of the criminal activities that the Singhs were involved in. She could not bring up the rape or assault as there was no evidence. Maya had to drop this case and concentrate solely on fighting for custody of the children. Maya could not get any results from the RCMP, they said they would help her, but no one from that department ever reached out to her again. Insp. Rahul Khan tried to get some of the officers in that department to assist, but it went nowhere. Finally, Maya just gave up and concentrated on getting full custody of the children.

Maya's grandmother, Betsy, would babysit the children whenever she had to go to court, which seemed to be every Friday for a whole day. Betsy would make *'pholourie and potato balls'* for the kids. They loved when she came to stay.

Maya was on first name basis with Insp. Rahul Khan by this time and he used to offer to take Maya to court. Maya was beginning to get very fond of him and they seemed to be getting along very well. Rahul was divorced with two children, an older boy, and a younger girl. He shared a house in Ajax with his sister. He visited his children every other Sunday, or as time permitted, due to his very unusual schedule as an immigration and drug officer with the RCMP. Sometimes he would share some of his undercover stories with Maya and her family. Maya knew that he was working as an undercover agent and was investigating a convenience store owner just a few blocks from where she lived. But other than that, Maya did not want to know — she had enough of that world and wanted to hear none of it. She had moved past such horrible things.

Chapter Twelve

The Devastating Truth

Maya had now returned to work, resuming her original job. She still had to go to court on a bi-weekly basis. After numerous family court appearances and several dollars spent, Maya was eventually granted full custody of the children. Jason and Sal got to see them every Wednesday and every other weekend. Rahul continued to visit them every week. Maya was slowly learning that she was safe again, her children were safe too.

That following year, the day before Valentine's Day, Maya was happy to receive a call from Rahul, who seemed to have something on his mind.

"Hello Maya," his voice was smooth and soft.

"Hi, Rahul, how are you?" Maya ached cheerfully.

"I am on top of the world, never been better," he always said this phrase, and it always made Maya smile.

"Listen, are you doing anything for Valentine's Day?" He asked easily.

Maya was taken aback — she did not expect this.

"I know it's Wednesday and the children will be with their dad, and I would love to take you out for dinner," he continued effortlessly.

"Umm. No, I don't. I didn't plan anything."

Maya had forgotten tomorrow was Valentine's Day.

"Well, no pressure, but I would love to take you out," Rahul said gently. His voice was persuasive.

"Can I think about it? I will let you know tomorrow morning," Maya answered nervously. Is he asking her on a date, or is it just friends hanging out?

She was confused, and a bit hesitant, but excited all at the same time.

"Absolutely!" he said, silver-tongued.

That night Maya could not sleep. She called her older sister.

"Hey, guess what?" Maya did not want to sound too enthusiastic or excited, but she did.

"What?" her sister said.

"Rahul wants to take me to dinner tomorrow for Valentine's, but I am not sure if I should go?" she said nervously, excited.

"Why not, just go, what do you have to lose," Rania said, sensing Maya's excitement. "Besides, he is damn good looking. I thought you would have gone out with him already, so just go!"

Maya was so nervous. She did not know what to wear, how to comb her hair, or what kind of makeup to wear. *Should she wear flats or heels? Would her high heel boots to be too much?* She realized this was the first date she had ever been on, yet she was unsure if it was an actual date.

She tried out about three sweaters and a pair of blue jeans.

She thought, *if a date is going to be perfect, there are three elements that need to be perfect: the person, the place and shared activity.*

They went to Red Lobster for dinner.

And just like that, it was the beginning of a healing journey for Maya. After escaping Jason's narcissistic and psychopathic personality, Maya needed to learn and understand that not all men were like that.

In Rahul, she found relief from solitude and loneliness. Her children found a father figure who was reliable, educated and always present. Their lives had finally settled into a normal routine, except for the ongoing custody battle. Maya did not see Jason much, as Sal always came to pick up and drop off the children. Maya was relieved that she did not have to deal with him. Maya never asked the children about their visits as they always came back distraught and unhappy. She did not want them to endure more unpleasantness, she did not want to disturb their minds and well-being more than was necessary.

It was not until years later, when the girls were teenagers, that they disclosed how Jason was rarely there when they visited. Apparently, most of the time, he was in drug rehabilitation. When he was home, he was abusive and violent to them, especially to Kyle. This knowledge came too late and made Maya so sad. She regretted not talking to the children about their visits.

But when it was their turn with the kids, Maya, and Rahul, who were now considered common-law, were a happy, loving, and well-established family. They bought a beautiful house near the lake. The children loved it. They loved taking the school bus in the mornings. Maya had tearfully said goodbye to Lori and taken a transfer east, making it much easier to commute and being at home on time for dinner and homework.

Ryder was now in Grade One, and Melena and Kyle were both doing well.

After Maya and Rahul moved in together, Jason had refused to come and pick up the children when it was his weekends to have them, so Sal asked if he could pick them up instead. Maya did not refuse. She knew how much Sal and Kayla enjoyed having them. Sal was getting to know Rahul, and they would stand outside and chat while Maya got the children ready for pickup.

Maya's whole life was different now. She was no longer spending every waking moment appeasing someone else for fear of their mood swings. Life was blissful. Maya's family was so happy for her, for how lucky she was to find such a loving and kind man who treats her children as if they were his own.

Although Rahul wanted to get married, Maya was pleased with the way things were. Still, he kept on pressuring her to get married – to have another child, and even persuading the children to "tell mommy we want another sibling."

After two years of living together, they finally decided to do it. Six weeks later, Maya was pregnant with their son, Sean. Her pregnancy was the most delightful experience in comparison what she endured with the other ones. Rahul treated her like royalty. She felt beautiful, loved, valued, and appreciated. He constantly told her how much he loved her. They were teammates in a beautiful, loving relationship. Indeed, Maya once again looked beautiful in her pregnancy, but this time she felt it to be true as well. Her hair had grown long to her waist again, and her skin was glowing and radiant. The children used to talk to baby, whom they named Sean in her belly through a paper towel roll. It was amusing. They were so excited and could not wait for Sean to arrive.

Kyle was the most excited to have a brother and wanted to share his room with the baby. Maya and Rahul explained the baby needed feeding at night and may sleep and cry most of the time. The baby won't be a playmate right away. The crib was set up in Rahul and Maya's room instead. They promised Kyle that he could share a room as soon as Sean was sleeping through the night.

This would give everyone a chance to get used to the new setup before dealing with the baby's arrival. Finally, the big day arrived. Maya's parents brought the children to the hospital for a brief visit. Maya's mom held Sean for a while so that Maya could give them plenty of cuddles, especially Ryder, who snuck up on the bed to be close to her mom. When Maya and Sean came home, Betsy moved in with them for a while to help prepare for the 'nine day.'

Before anything could be done, Betsy gave the baby a bath, decked him out in the 'nine-day' outfit that Premika made, and took him outside to see the sun. Betsy did the *'puja'* in the yard, and then they all headed back in, to cook and celebrate. The *'nine day'* — a celebration when the baby turns nine days old, and guests bring gifts, including gold bracelets for the baby. It was an affair to remember with live music, dancing, food, and drinking *'daru.'* Betsy made *'halwa and puri,'* and Rahul bought a whole goat to make 'goat curry' to go with the homemade *'dhal puri.'* There was *'chicken curry,' 'duck curry' rice, 'dhal.'* The ladies were making 'wicked jokes' and just having a grand old time. Betsy stayed a while to help with the children, who didn't want to stop holding the baby, cuddling him for hours on end. Melena insisted on feeding him his bottle every night. Although Rahul was working long hours, he made it home every night to put Sean to bed. Sean would fall asleep on his chest, and then Rahul would put him in the crib.

Maya and Rahul's lives centered around the children. Weekday routines were the same most days. Maya would leave for work at 6.00 am, and Rahul would get the kids dressed for school and see them off to the bus stop before dropping Sean off at the babysitter across the street. Then he would head for work at the RCMP base in the east. Maya would be back home just in time to get the children from the bus, pick up Sean and start dinner while the kids did homework and took their showers. Dinner would be ready just in time for when Rahul got home from work. Although he missed dinner on some occasions due to undercover work, their family routine was perfect. Life could not have been happier for Maya.

Weekends involved many outings and trips to the beach, the farm, and long countryside drives. Ryder and Melena were the entertainers of the family. On their long drives, they would have Maya play songs by Backstreet Boys and NSync. They would pretend they had microphones and sing loudly in the back of the minivan, keeping Kyle and Sean entertained the whole trip. Of course, Kyle, being the older, 'cooler' one, would laugh and teasingly call them 'losers.'

Maya was pleased to see how happy they were, as she knew they do not get to be themselves when they visit their dad at Kayla and Sal's. The love and attention that Rahul showered upon her, and the children was beyond her imagination. Rahul was terrific with the kids. He used to braid Melena's long hair every morning before school and even taught Kyle how to read the Holy Quran. It was such a lovely sight to see how they bonded. The children were even calling him 'dad.' Rahul had decided to see his children on weekends they had Maya's children. On the other weekends, while they were at Jason's, Maya and Rahul had some free time to themselves.

Eventually, Rahul stopped seeing his children altogether. He said that his ex-wife had moved, and it was a far drive to see them so often. He said that now that the children were teenagers, they were not really interested in seeing him that often. Maya had insisted on Rahul keeping a relationship with his children. But Rahul changed the topic every time she tried to bring it up. Maya finally gave up.

Maya and Rahul had just returned with the children from a three-week long vacation to Trinidad. This was the third trip here, and Rahul was very well known as "King Khan" in the Port of Spain, having lived there for some time in his late twenties after leaving the Canadian Armed Forces. He had come back to Trinidad to train the Trinidad and Tobago Defence Force (TTDF) before returning to Canada to join the RCMP.

This trip was mainly for vacation as they wanted Sean to meet his paternal grandmother and aunts. They had rented a car at the airport and had decided to rent a house in Carenage, near the yacht club. The children wanted to come back to the same place they were last time, since they loved it so much. They would take daily trips to Maracas Beach with Rahul's family or visit all the local tourist attractions. In the evenings, they would go to the drive-in cinema in Valsayn, where they watched the same Bollywood movie "Koyla," five days in a row, but they did not care. It became Kyle's favorite Bollywood movie. Maya was sure it was not the movie, but the great memories he had on their vacation, that made him love it. Other evenings they would go to the Savannahs to buy coconut water and enjoy the steel pan bands, preparing for the Carnival festival. Soca and chutney music was blaring everywhere. It was a lovely time, a festive time, and the children were thoroughly enjoying themselves.

Upon returning from Trinidad, Maya and Rahul began making plans to purchase a newly built home. They would go visit sites when the children stayed with Kayla and Sal. They wanted to surprise the children. They were all going to get their own bedrooms. Maya and Rahul decided to move Northeast. It was close to both their workplaces, and it was a newly built neighborhood. They chose a gated community and a beautiful contemporary design home, which would be ready just in time for them to move so the children could start fall classes at the new school. Maya was elated as she picked out paint colors, tile designs, patio stones, and bathroom fixtures.

Maya was heavily involved in the United Way Campaigns at Work and was the Events coordinator. They were having a dinner and awards ceremony that fall and Maya asked Rahul to accompany her since she was an award recipient. Maya, planning to introduce Rahul to her colleagues at the dinner event, was upset when Rahul suddenly had to go see his son for a family emergency, missing the event entirely. After dinner, she realized that she should not be upset. Instead, she should be supportive as Rahul has been to her.

Her colleagues encouraged her to go to Rahul's sister's house to show her support and love. So, Maya headed home and called Rahul several times, but he did not answer. She was beginning to get worried. Finally, on her sixteenth time trying, a woman answered. Maya assumed it was Rahul sister.

"Hi Carly, it's Maya," she stated.

She could hear Rahul in the background saying, "Give me the phone, give me the phone," urgently. He seemed to be fumbling to get the phone from the woman who answered it.

"Who are you," the woman who Maya thought was Carly, asked.

"It's Maya, Rahul's wife," she answered.

"You can't be his wife, I am his wife," the woman said.

"What?" Maya asked, "Oh, you must be Rahul's ex-wife. Is everything okay?"

"I am not his ex-wife, I am his wife," the woman stated firmly.

"There must be a misunderstanding, I am sorry," Maya said. "I understand you have his children, but I am his wife now."

Rahul seemed to be fumbling to take the phone, still saying, "give me the damn phone."

"Look woman, I don't know who you are, or what you think you are doing, but I am Mrs. Khan, Rahul's wife for more than twenty years. Not his ex-wife, but his wife. I don't know what you want, but do not call this number again." She hung up the phone.

Maya was shocked and puzzled. She tried several times to call again but got no response. She sat on the floor in her bedroom in shock, numb, and frozen with dread.

It dawned on Maya that she was *the other woman.*

She quickly got up and went over to Rahul's night table. He kept it locked as he holds the gun in there. Maya was always concerned about this and was thankful that he was cautious to keep it locked, so the children couldn't access it. However, on one occasion, he had left it open, and it alarmed her. She has seen files, an agenda, and a phone book in there. However, she did not open anything. Maya believed it to be Rahul's undercover work and did not go through it. Maya grabbed a letter opener and open the drawer. She leafed through the address book and found many contact details in Rahul's phone book. She flipped through it and found a contact for Andre, his son, who was about nineteen now. Assuming it was Andre's phone number and address, she scribbled it down and called the number. No answer. She called again, still no response. She looked at the address, it was not far from their house. A few blocks, maybe. She was puzzled. Maybe Andre moved here. Rahul never mentioned that he did, though.

And then the doorbell rang. Maya didn't think Rahul would ring the doorbell. Did he forget his keys? It was Sal with the kids. Maya had lost track of time. He said the kids were bathed, fed and ready for bed after a long day at the zoo.

Maya was still shocked and nodded her head. Kyle sensed her uneasiness and helped her with Ryder as they got ready for bed.

"Where is dad," He asked, referring to Rahul.

"He is at work, he should be back soon," Maya quickly replied. She tucked Melena and Ryder in bed and turned to Kyle.

"Look, mommy has to go to the corner store, can you look after Melena and Ryder for me? I will be right back."

"Sure, mom." He was always so helpful.

Maya grabbed her keys and ran out of the house, not even bothering to put shoes on. She drove to the address that she had scribbled down and rang the doorbell. Maya was horrified to be met at the door by a woman in a pink nightie. It was not Carly. This must be his ex-wife, Kate. Rahul was standing behind her.

"Who are you?" the woman asked.

"I am... Um, he knows who I am," Maya said hesitantly, not sure what to do or say. She ran her hand through her hair nervously. "Ask him."

To Maya's dismay, Rahul just stood there.

"I am his wife," Maya said defensively.

"Can't be honey, you must be mad. This is my husband, and this is our home," the woman said mockingly. "You need to leave."

"I am not leaving until he explains what is going on," Maya said defiantly.

"If you don't leave now, I will call the police," the woman stated.

"I am not leaving. Call the police, let him explain two wives," Maya insisted, shaking nervously.

"Katie, go get my gun, I'll shoot her if she does not leave," Rahul finally spoke.

Maya could not believe her ears. Astonishment and disbelief hit her like a ton of bricks. Devastated and astound, Maya realized that Rahul was still living with Kate. Thrown for a loop by this revelation, Maya accidentally broke one of Kate's garden urns as she staggered back to the car, embarrassed and in complete shock.

All her life's pain and trauma came rushing back. Maya felt out of control. Here was this man whom she thought genuinely loved her, who sincerely cared for her and for her children. She could not help thinking about what a fool she had been. Maya was crushed. She felt like her heart had been ripped from her body and shattered into tiny little pieces. She had this image of Rahul as her prince charming, swooping in to take her away from all her pain and misery. Little did she realize that Rahul was abusing her, emotionally. He was a narcissist who manipulated her thoughts and her feelings. He made their life look like it was out of a fairy tale, and he was her knight in shining armor.

He would boast to her sisters how "he saved her." What would she tell everyone now? Her heart cried, and her eyes filled with tears as well. She had given him everything: her heart, her soul, her smile, her body, and dignity, and for the first time in her life, her love. Sorrowfully she thought, *I even gave him my children.*

Maya was faithful to their love. She was loyal to him and did not see this coming. Not in a million years. Was all this a mistake? Was this just a game to Rahul? How was her life once again filled with lies and deceit? How could he do this to her?

Maya sat in the minivan, still parked on Kate's driveway, her feet shaking too much that she didn't trust herself to drive. She sat there for over fifteen minutes, shaking uncontrollably. She was shivering, despite the hot temperature outside. She hugged herself to stop from shaking, and then covered her face with her hands. She felt so ashamed, so lost, so embarrassed. How could she have been so foolish? There was a knock on the window. Maya looked up. It was Rahul. She rolled down the window, still trembling in shock.

"Maya, why did you come here? Why did you want to hurt yourself like that?" he asked sadly.

"What the hell is going on Rahul, what are you doing here?" Maya demanded.

"I can't explain now, Maya, you have to leave, you have to go home." He was still gentle, almost kind.

"Rahul, please, what is happening," Maya asked hysterically.

"Maya, please go home. I will come in the morning."

"In the morning, why?" Maya was so confused.

"I will fix everything in the morning, now go," he insisted.

Maya put the car in reverse and almost knocked him over. She was home in two minutes. She quickly ran upstairs. Kyle was watching TV. Melena, Ryder, and Sean all fast asleep.

"Mom, you okay?" Kyle asked, concerned.

"Yes baby, let's get you to bed.

"Where is dad?" he asked.

"He is at work."

Maya tucked him in and went to her room. She showered, barely thinking what she was doing, almost in a trance. Maya lay on the bed, and then tears came, then sobbing. She quickly got up and locked herself in the walk-in closet.

The sobbing didn't stop. After almost two hours, Maya was finally exhausted and fell asleep on the floor in the closet.

Chapter Thirteen

The Ugly...the Bad... the Good

Maya abruptly jumped out of an exhausted state and realized she was sleeping in the closet. Her mind was racing, thoughts zipping through her head like a movie in fast forward.

He said he was going to shoot me!
What do I really know about this man?
Why didn't Carly say anything?
Why didn't his family in Trinidad say anything? We just saw them only a month ago.
What if he comes in the house and murders all of us?
Who is he? Is his name really Rahul Khan? Is he really an RCMP Inspector?

Oh my god, I left my children with him.
He has keys to the house. He has a gun!
He could shoot us all.

Her thoughts were going so fast in her head. It felt as if her head was about to explode. She took a few deep breaths and tried to get up, but her knees felt weak.

She took a few more deep breaths and managed to get up and wash her face. *Think Maya! Think! You must protect your children,* she told herself. She grabbed the phone and dialed 911.

"My husband threatened to shoot me," she exclaimed.

The Police took a statement, and within minutes they were at the door.

She did not want them to knock, so she waited at the door. The police officers that came were very kind. When she mentioned Rahul's name, they recognized "Insp. Rahul" immediately. They asked her if she wanted to press charges. Maya was so confused; her mind was in a chaotic state.

"How do you press charges on a police officer?"

The officers assured her that she could, especially if she felt threatened. Maya was not sure what she felt. *Was Rahul in trouble?* He seemed very distressed. *What if she was jumping the gun? Would it cost him his job? Would they be able to afford the house, the legal fees?*

"Can I sleep on it?" She asked the officers.

"Yes, but will you be okay tonight," one officer asked.

"Can I get the house keys from him?" she asked.

"Is this his house too?" the officer asked.

"It is in my name only," Maya answered.

They had bought the house in her name because Rahul felt that after all that she had gone through with Jason, she would have something of her own. Little did Maya know that he already had another house, and that was just an excuse so she would not find out about the other place he had with Kate. The officers offered to go and get the keys. They returned within minutes stating that he was very cooperative.

The next day was Saturday. Maya made breakfast for the children, and then they went to the backyard to play.

Rahul called, and Kyle answered.

"Dad says he will be home soon," he said happily.

Maya was anxious, edgy. Minutes later, Rahul came around the back, his face drawn, strained. He looked tired and haggard. He hugged the kids and kissed Sean on the forehead. Maya stared at him blankly. To her, he looked different, like an unfamiliar person — a stranger.

Rahul tried to explain to Maya that he had gone back to Kate and the children right before they went to Trinidad. He wanted to stay with Kate as his daughter, Emily, had just been diagnosed with a brain tumor. Maya's heart immediately went out to him. She felt so remorseful and apologetic. *No wonder he looked so drained*, Maya thought. She felt sorry for him. The sparkle in his eyes was gone.

"Why didn't you say something," she asked.

"I didn't want to lose you. I was afraid," he explained.

"Why would you lose me if your daughter is sick?" she asked. Thank goodness she did not press charges. She felt wretched and regretful. She shouldn't have called the Police.

"I didn't know what to do at the time, and that's why I wanted to go away, to think," he explained.

"Rahul, how could you even have thought to go away at such a time," Maya scolded.

"I needed a break. I needed to clear my head, and I wanted just to be with you and the kids at the time," he tried to explain.

"So, what are you going to do? Are you leaving us?" Maya questioned.

"No, no Maya, I love you. I love Sean and the children. You are my life, I can't." He was so tense.

"So, what then, I really don't know what you want me to say?" Maya questioned. "I understand that you need to be there for your daughter, but we are your family too, you can't have two homes."

"I have to share myself between you and them. I promised my daughter I would be there for her."

"I totally understand Rahul, but what does that actually mean?" Maya was surprised that she was so calm.

"I will always come home every night. No matter how late, but I must be there for Emily, too." He replied, his eyes looking at her with uncertainty.

Maya nodded, trying to wrap her head around what was happening. How could she keep him away from his dying daughter? She had to try and get a grip of this situation, what he was telling her, and what their life would be. She feared that he was a liar. That he, too, was deceitful, just like Jason. She shook her head, trying to get rid of such thoughts. It's not fair to Rahul. She needed to be positive for him, to be his support, his strength.

"Okay, you have no choice, you need to be there for her, we will be fine," Maya said positively.

For the next two weeks, Rahul felt like a stranger to her. Like a guest. He came home after the children were in bed. Maya was exhausted, as Sean was having a difficult time falling asleep. He was so used to falling asleep on Rahul's chest at night. After almost two weeks of trying to put him down and getting him to fall asleep without crying, Maya had finally found a way for him to fall asleep without Rahul. She would take him to the jacuzzi tub and have a bath with him. The humming of the jets would put him to sleep, and Melena would take him to the bed and get him dressed in his PJs while Maya finished up in the bath. By the time Maya was out, Sean would be fast asleep.

Going into the third week, Maya still would not let Rahul touch her. She felt uneasy. He begged to make love to her, but she could not. She could not even let him kiss her, his lips felt different, his touch felt altered and impure. Maya was having a difficult time in her own head, she had no ability to focus or concentrate, and she was unable to work.

One Saturday night, Rahul came home before 9pm and went straight to the shower. Maya was watching TV in the bedroom after having just put the children to bed. She looked at his phone on the table. She had never invaded his privacy, never even thought to look at his phone before. He had never given her any reason to do so. She picked up the phone and scrolled through it, not sure what she was looking for. She saw Andre's number and quickly memorized it. As Rahul came out of the shower, she went to Kyle's room to get a pen. Not finding one, she grabbed a crayon and wrote the number behind the door and covered it with Kyle's bath towel.

That night she was especially uncomfortable with Rahul in the bed and asked if he could sleep on the couch instead. After some hesitation, he went downstairs.

The next day Maya called Andre.

"Hi, my name is Maya. Do you remember me?"

"Yes." He remembered her when she came to see his wrestling match some years ago, when she and Rahul were first dating. Another time she had gone with Rahul to take Andre to the army base in Petawawa where he was training. Maya asked how his sister was doing. He seemed puzzled but said that they were both doing well.

"How is her brain tumour, did she have the surgery yet?" Maya asked.

"What tumor, what are you talking about?" he responded.

"Your dad said that Emily is dying from a brain tumor."

"What?! What the heck are you talking about. My sister is fine, in fact, she just started university in Waterloo," he stated. Maya felt faint.

"Listen, can I meet you?" Maya asked.

"Sure, I will be home from university tomorrow."

"I can meet you at the Tim Hortons at the corner of Harwood and Westley Road, say 6:00 pm," Maya said quickly, hoping he would not change his mind.

"Yes, sure," he said. "6:00pm, Timmies."

He hung up.

That night Maya could not bear to look at Rahul. Her love for him had diminished. She felt used, devalued, and spent. She could not sleep all night. Who was lying? Rahul? Andre? Who is deceiving her? How could anyone lie about a dying child? Especially Rahul. He was too kind; he was a good man.

Andre was right on time. Maya had asked Rania to take care of the children, and she brought Sean with her.

"This is your brother," she introduced Sean to Andre. He stared at her in disbelief.

"Your dad didn't tell you that you had a brother?" She asked, remembering that Rahul had said Andre was furious that he had started a family, which is why he had moved away.

They talked for almost two hours.

Andre did not know he had a brother, nor did he move away because of Sean. He had started a degree in Forensic Science at the University of Toronto and was staying on campus. Andre appeared extremely upset about the fact that his dad lied about his sister dying. He said that was unacceptable. During their lengthy conversation, Andre confirmed that his father and mother never separated, never had a divorce. Although Rahul was away a lot, Andre said he was always there almost every day at home for dinner. Andre claimed that Rahul did work long hours and did leave most nights after dinner to go back to work. He claimed to have to do night surveillance, but he was there, at home, as a good father and a good husband.

Maya was baffled. How did Rahul do this? He was also there for them most days for dinner, outings, children's school recitals, and family gatherings. He never missed any family get-together. In fact, Maya's sisters teased him, that he was stuck to her like glue and never left her alone. Maya enjoyed the attention as she never had that before.

Rahul took the children to school every day and Sean to Montessori school. They went on vacation for weeks at a time. How is this possible? It is impossible. Who was lying? She shared the dates of their vacations to Trinidad with Andre, and they realized that some of their vacation times in Trinidad overlapped! Even the most recent one, last month!

"Mother fucker!" Maya swore under her breath. She does not usually curse.

Apparently, Rahul told Kate he did not want to stay with her family in Trinidad. Obviously, this caused some conflicts between them. Although he did spend some days with them, Andre recalled that Rahul never stayed overnight at Andre's grandparents' home in Trinidad, claiming he would be staying at his mother's place instead. It seemed that those days he spent with Kate and her family, he told Maya that he was visiting some buddies at the police station. Rahul was once in charge of Trinidad and Tobago Police Services Tactical Squad, National Security, and still had many friends on the force.

During the days that Maya spent at the beach with the children and his family, Rahul was spending time with Kate and her family. Rahul's web of lies was slowly being unraveled. As Maya and Andre sipped coffee and caught their breaths, they realized even more overlapping lies – it seemed that Rahul often would not stop at just one lie and end up telling more to cover for the others. It was a habit that seemed to make his life even trickier, as he must have had to remember all his lies to keep up with the various stories.

Maya and Andre then circled back to talking about Sean. Andre wanted to know if Maya would allow him to see Sean when he visited from university. Maya agreed. This young man seemed distraught at his father's deception and lies. Rahul was lying to everyone. They spoke about how close their houses were and how come they never ran into each other.

Maya realized that the reason Rahul never let her do the shopping is not that she "had too many things to do without worrying about shopping," as he put it. He probably never wanted her to run into Kate or anyone else for that matter.

The biggest bombshell was when Andre told Maya that his parents were moving to Whitby and that they had put a down payment on a new home being built there. Maya almost fell off her chair. It was the same house, the same down payment that came out of her account for their dream house. What was Rahul doing? What the hell was he thinking? Was he planning on moving them both to the same house? Maya was more confused and puzzled than ever. Tears ensued. Andre was adamant that Rahul and Kate never broke up and was Maya obstinate in letting him know that she and Rahul have had a life together for so many years.

Maya's realization that she had been the *other woman*, the *mistress*, was sinking in. Unknowingly to her, Rahul had made her "that woman," the woman having an extramarital sexual relationship with a married man. Maya bade farewell to Andre, and they promised to stay in touch, as he wanted to see Sean every other weekend. Maya went home and made dinner for the children. Rahul had called to say he would be late. She didn't answer but let it go to the machine. Maya knew that she could not carry on in this relationship with Rahul. She had never given him back house keys. That night, he did not come home.

The next day she called a family meeting with her parents and sisters. She didn't go to them last time, but this time was different. She needed them now more than ever.

The Ugly Truth

Maya sat in the kitchen of her parents' home. It was a bright Sunday afternoon. They had just finished dinner, although Maya was not in the mood to eat. Her father and brother-in-law were watching TV with the kids in the family room. Rania and Daya were clearing the dishes and putting away the food. Her mother sat at the kitchen table, pensive. Maya began talking about what happened. Everyone was in disbelief when she told them that Rahul was still with his wife and children.

Maya's mom said "It's not easy, as a mother, to see your child go through anything like this. This is just so painful. You've had two unhealthy relationships in a row now."

All night before, Maya thought of everything that happened to her, all her childhood trauma and sexual abuse when she was pregnant with Kyle and Ryder. She knew that her task now was to talk through those emotions and let her family know what happened, so Maya exhaled, and everything poured out. Maya finally got up the nerve to tell her mother about Khalil, about how he had sexually molested her for years.

"I've been fine for years. Now everything is coming back, crashing down on me. I have nightmares every night and can barely function," she said sadly. "I thought I was over it. Now everything is all coming back. My trauma started years ago, with Khalil."

Her mom looked puzzled.

"What do you mean?"

"Mom, I was fifteen when he left for Trinidad, that is when it stopped," Maya said tearfully. "Why do you think that all these years I had refused to call him uncle?"

For years Maya had avoided this man who abused her at family functions and gatherings. She would instead call him a family member because uncle is a title, he had lost the right to, when he sexually molested her.

Maya knew that all that happened later in her life, after the passage of time and blocking the trauma out, meant that she could not remember everything that happened clearly. She does not know the exact dates but knows the sexual molestation she endured was inflicted on her numerous times. Her abuser carried out his crimes when no one else was around – when her grandparents were busy working, or the other siblings were outside. It was kept entirely secret from other members of the family. She can, however, pinpoint the abuse to happening in a span of seven years, beginning in the 1970s, because she remembers the house in the village, where it happened, and how it had impacted her life.

As she sat in that room, telling her story for the first time, it reopened a chapter of her life she had kept buried for so many years.

"I felt damaged, and I never really recognized that what was done to me had caused me so much trauma. How it has damaged me so badly. It happened to me repeatedly. It traumatized me so badly, to a point of controlling my children as well."

Her children, especially the girls, were not allowed to sleep over anywhere. She was highly protective of them for fear something would happen to them. She took them everywhere they had to go. Her family now knew what happened. Maya was conflicted in the thought that her mother did not believe her. Sadly, for this reason, she did not tell them about Jason and Mark. Although her family never talked about it again and seem to avoid it when Maya tried to bring it up, Maya was relieved she told them. Khalil never admitted what he had done, even when asked directly by Betsy, and to this day, Maya's parents haven't spoken about it again.

In the first few days after the family meeting, Maya shut down because the emotions were so overwhelming, and she could not deal with them all at once. All those pent-up feelings and emotions come roaring back.

Why now? Why are these feelings and memories coming back now? Maya kept asking herself.

Maya asked Rahul to stay away from then on, that she needed time to think, to clear her head. She did not take any of Rahul's calls. Maya knew that she needed to heal. She did not want to hear his lies; she did not even want to listen to his voice. She did not trust him. He even tried calling her parents, but everyone just shut him out. She realized her whole life with Rahul was a big game to him. She misplaced her love and trust. She had trusted this man who ended up ripping her soul apart. For many years after that, Maya had a hard time trusting anyone. She was bitter and torn.

Several weeks went by, and Maya tried getting in touch with Kate to tell her side of the story and to hear Kate's side as well. She wanted answers. She never got them. Kate refused to speak with her, and Andre never kept his promise to see Sean. That plan only lasted for a month or so. Maya did not blame him, he obviously needed to stick with his mother. But Maya was angry, her vengeance was compelling. Her anger was building up more and more as the days went by. She was snapping at the children and was constantly feeling on edge. Her sleep was poor, and she was getting irritated easily. She was becoming frustrated and irritable at minor things. One day, she snapped at Kyle, to then realize all he wanted was to show her a book.

That day, she decided to let go, to get rid of everything that reminded her of Rahul and their time together. It was a Wednesday, and Sal had picked up the children after school. It was just Maya and Sean. Maya looked around the house and realized that everything in her and the children's life revolved around Rahul. Family portraits that he had insisted they took every year, spread through the living room walls. She jumped into action, her energy pumping with pent-up anger, and started pulling all the portraits from the walls. Maya threw them in a box, found all the photo albums, and ripped Rahul out of every picture. She packed all of Rahul's things in boxes, loaded them into the back of the minivan, buckled in Sean, and drove over to Kate's house. Although she felt like a mad woman, she calmly unpacked all the boxes, dropped them at the front door, and rang the doorbell before getting back into the van and driving off.

Then she was done! She vowed that no one would ever be allowed to hurt her again. Love was bullshit. Survival was everything. Maya knew that she needed to get up, brush it off and move on. As difficult as it was, she felt renewed and empowered, and even a sudden need to heal and be herself, be an independent woman. She was ready to heal on a deeper level.

Her scars made her strong. She needed to make plans to move on with her life. She needed to be strong, to survive, to be a mother and father to four children. Maya knew financially she was able enough to pay the bills, the mortgage, and the car payments. She may not be able to afford to send Sean to Montessori school, but her kind neighbors had offered to babysit. Maya knew she could do this.

Maya and the children started going to temple on Sundays and volunteering in the kitchen after service. During the week, after work, she would delve into renovating the house with the kids, making it fun for them to pull down wallpaper and rip up carpets. She made it like a game for them. She was done with crying and feeling sorry for herself. All the pain and trauma were behind her now.

Twenty-five years later, she still volunteers for the temple. It is part of her own journey to heal and be free of trauma. Maya's volunteer journey led to teaching the children of the temple dances and theatre. Even Melena and Ryder were enjoying dance classes, and Maya realized that she too had been missing dance in her life. Dance, which once was a burning fire in her heart a very long time ago, was pushed aside during all of life's trials and tribulations. But now, her passion for dance was surfacing again, and it seemed to be the piece of the puzzle she was missing as she became more focused on her independence. Dance was her truest expression of herself, it was etched into her being, her identity, and her sense of self. When Maya was asked to become a volunteer dance instructor at the temple, she quickly jumped at the opportunity, giving her time and energy to her love of movement. This also helped her start teaching and sharing her passion with Melena and Ryder, and even Sean. Kyle didn't care for dance, but he became very involved in basketball.

This led to Maya eventually owning a professional dance school of her own.

Chapter Fourteen

Serendipity

Years later, after endless court battles for custody of the children, it finally ended when Sal passed away. Ryder was eighteen at the time, and although Sal had no grounds to fight for Kyle and Melena, he was still going at it to get Ryder. Life at home was safe and stable, and even happy.

Maya had resigned to be alone for the rest of her life. However, she was not exactly sitting around with nothing to do. She was busy with her volunteer work, the dance school, a wedding decorating business, and a full-time job. Who had time for dating?

Kyle and Melena were both in relationships and had moved out on their own. Ryder and Sean were still at home. Life was good. That winter, Sean got a cat, Charlotte, for Christmas from his aunt

Daya. He was so happy, and Charlotte seemed to bring even more love into the household.

On their usual weekend get-togethers, her nieces and her daughters would tease Maya. They would laughingly tell her that she would become a crazy cat lady if she did not start dating. One evening, they were having wine and cheese, and they decided to set Maya up on Match.com. Maya thought it was funny. They asked her questions about what she would want in a man. Maya playfully went along with it. She certainly did not take it seriously.

"I want a man who is genuine and kind and most importantly, truthful," she said honestly.

Her online profile read: "I've been on so many blind dates I could get a free dog. AKA 'The Real Thing.'"

Over the next few months, Maya did go on a few failed and futile dates. One guy had nine children with four different "baby mamas" and was just looking for another. Another guy was the father of one of Kyle's friends. After speaking with Kyle about it, Maya found out that he was still living with his wife. Another guy told her that his mother and daughter would always come first and if they shared a house, his mother deserves the master bedroom, and they would have to live in the basement. She gave up and stopped looking at the notifications from Match.com.

Maya was furious after her last date and confided in Daya, "These people weren't necessarily looking for a relationship, they are focused on finding someone to fulfill themselves."

Serendipity

Maya had sworn off online dating for good, but Nadia, Daya and her daughters didn't let her give up so easily, leading her once again into cyberspace to find her perfect match.

As the six-month subscription was coming to an end and Maya was looking to close the account, an amazing man fell into her life when she least expected it. Maya and Scott met on the last day of her Match.com subscription. What a coincidence it was. To this day their refer to their meeting as 'click for love.' She remembers it fondly.

Maya and Daya volunteer at the temple to decorate the stage for cultural events and shows. They share a large office with traditional Indian decor and a smattering of brightly colored sarees and prints spread over a small sofa, paintings of Hindu gods and deities hung from the walls.

Maya was running late that morning after a disastrous blind date the night before.

"You're almost late, that's not like you," Daya said.

Maya sat down her latte and peered over the top of the particle board wall that separated their desks.

"I hit snooze."

"That'll do it," Daya replied nonchalantly.

"You had better get it together. We have less than four hours to finish the decorations on the stage before preparing the final program for tomorrow's 'Holi' show."

"I don't know what has gotten into me," Maya commented as she picked up the sarees to pack in the container to take to the temple.

"Maybe your blind date last night?"

Maya winched.

"Oh yeah thanks for reminding me," she hurried to power up her computer to prepare the program.

"No wonder I am zoned out. I barely survived another blind date. I've got to cancel my account right now."

"That bad huh?"

"Yes, it was horrible, and where were you? I tried sending you a distress signal!!"

"Oops! Sorry, I was having a late dinner with Asam."

"That Wally character was a real winner," Maya said sarcastically. "I am done with online dating!"

"Done?"

"D-O-N-E!!" Maya spelled out clearly as she tapped on her keyboard.

"Come on, it couldn't be as bad as the guy who had nine kids."

"Thanks for reminding me about that one! His profile said he was a father! How was I to know he had nine kids with four different women!"

"We seemed so perfect for each other and then this random guy shows up and was nothing like his profile described, the bastards all lie in their profiles."

As they headed out the door, containers of sarees in hand, Maya realized that she had forgotten to press enter on her computer to delete the online dating account.

That evening after an exhausting day of decorating, Maya sat down on her sofa with a glass of her favorite wine. She decided to reach for her laptop and finish deleting the account before finalizing the Holi Show program. There were seven notifications of likely matches for Maya. As she continued to delete the notifications, she noticed one match that caught her eye. His picture profile showed him as blond, with a goatee, blue eyes, and over six feet tall.

"Hmmm, blond, I never dated a blonde before, but I like the goatee," Maya thought with a smile. So, she opened his message.

Scott: "Good evening, 'The Real Thing,' nice to virtually meet you. From your profile picture you seem happy and contented."

Maya smiled and placed her elbows on the coffee table, resting her chin in her fists, contemplating if she should reply. She glanced at Charlotte sitting on the sofa next to her.

"What do you think girly?"

The cat's ears perked up at its mistress's question. Maya smiled and looked back at the screen. She clicked on the red flashing icon and began to type.

The Real Thing: "Have we met?"

Maya watched the screen waiting for a reply. It didn't take long.

Scott: "We have now."

The Real Thing: "Touché. What brings you to this site?"

Scott: "I am new to this thing. My friends told me it is a good way to meet locals."

The Real Thing: "Can I ask you something?"

Scott: "What would you like to know?"

The Real Thing: "If you were a candy bar, what would it be?"

Maya waited, imaging this handsome, blue-eyed man sitting in front of his computer, thinking of an answer. She smiled at Charlotte.

Scott: "I have never thought about it, but maybe a healthy bar."

The Real Thing: "Mmm. Decadent."

Scott: "My turn. If you're stranded on a deserted island and could only have one item, what would it be?"

The Real Thing: "That's easy my computer."

Scott. "No Internet."

The Real Thing: "That's not fair! Can I change my answer?"

Scott: "No."

The Real Thing: "No?"

Scott: "Is that your question?"

The Real Thing: "No. Here's mine. If your house was on fire and you could only save one thing, what would it be?"

Scott: "That's easy, my CD collections."

The Real Thing: "Really?"

Maya thought this was interesting as she too would save her music collection.

Scott: "Yes, I love music and cherish my collections. Look, The Real Thing, we could stay online exchanging silly questions back and forth, and we won't really get to know each other any better. If you really want to know me, all you have to do is ask. I'm on this site because I thought this could be an excellent way to meet some locals and get to know the city better, but it has not really worked in my favor. I'd like to get to know you better. I am getting off this site, as this is my last day. Maybe we can exchange phone numbers?"

Maya thought, what a coincidence as she was on the computer to delete her account!

The Real Thing: "So what brings you to this city?"

Scott: "Work, And I should probably get back to it."

The Real Thing: "Must be computer-based."

Scott: "Somewhat."

The Real Thing: "Your candor intrigues me. I'm here looking for friendship. I have never met a true match, and I haven't had much luck with online dating either. Coincidentally, it is also my last day on this site. I'm not sure if there is such a perfect match, but if you want to be friends, I don't mind exchanging numbers."

Scott: "That would be great. I was taking a break and surfing the net. I would love to chat with you all night, but tomorrow is an early day for me. I'm going to have to click out of here now. Here's my number, maybe we can chat again sometime on the phone."

The Real Thing: "I'd like that. Here is mine."

Maya looked at the computer screen, and Scott's red flashing lights stop blinking. Feeling her eyelids becoming heavy, Maya took one last look at the draft Holi program. And with a few clicks of the mouse, powered her computer down. She stepped from the sofa, motioning Charlotte to follow. Her smiled lingered as she settled into her plush bedding with her beloved cat nestled quietly beside her.

The following day, she got a message on her phone.

Scott: "If you were breakfast, what would you be?"

The Real Thing: "Fruit loops, you?"

Scott: "Bran cereal."

The Real Thing: "To keep you regular?"

Scott: "Gives me strength."

The Real Thing: "I've got to go; I'll check with you later. Currently, I'm surrounded by muscle bound moving men."

Scott: "There's a dilemma for a single girl. Are you going somewhere?"

The Real Thing: "Just moving to a new office. Can we chat later?"

A few weeks went by, and despite their hectic schedules, they managed to chat with each other every evening. They had planned to meet for coffee, but Maya was planning a trip to Trinidad for Carnival with Daya, Asam, and their friends, and Scott was going back to Germany to attend his sister's wedding. They both thought it would be best if they met after the trips.

Maya was the only single one in the travelling the group, but it didn't bother her. She had gotten used to being Daya and Asam's 'third wheel,' and they never left her out of anything. Vacations, social events, and friends gathering, she was always invited.

That trip made Maya realized that she had begun to like Scott and could not wait to return so that they can get to know each other more. She realized she was starting to open her heart again, and she was scared, but she was also intrigued. After they both returned, the first thing Scott said on their call was, "you are too nice of a lady to take for coffee, I want to make you dinner, would you let me?"

Maya was bowled over by his kind and genuine nature.

Scott was hunched over the butcher block, locked in deep concentration, carefully chopping the broccoli with a gleaming stainless-steel knife. The aroma of garlic simmering with butter in a cast-iron pan filled the house. He added the broccoli to the garlic mixture, threw in a handful of sweet red pepper for more color, and gently shook the pan to evenly coat the vegetables.

Turning the heat down before returning the pot to the burner, Scott suddenly realized that something was missing. He stood still in the center of the kitchen, going over every detail, then snapped his fingers and walked into the living room, where he gently placed a CD into the stereo and hit play. The sweet melodies of Bob Marley's reggae music filled the air. Before heading back to the kitchen, he pulled a bottle of Cabernet Sauvignon from the wine rack. After uncorking the wine, he poured a splash into a giant crystal wine glass and swirled it slowly, savoring the rich bouquet and color. Finally, everything is ready for Maya's arrival.

The overhead light had been dimmed, and lit candles were placed on a table set romantically for two. The flame shimmered across the silver place settings of white China. Rich scents of garlic butter and wine mixed with the sweet sounds of slow reggae music enveloped the space like a warm blanket.

All the details combined hinted, like foreplay, at things to come. Hearing the doorbell, Scott wiped his hands on a dishcloth and quickly went to the foyer. Opening the door, his heart skipped a beat. Maya looked stunning. She took his breath away.

"Hello Scott," her sweet voice like a soft melody.

Serendipity

"Hi Maya, it's nice to finally meet you, welcome to my humble abode," opening the door wider, he swept his arms in a flourish and stepped aside, allowing Maya to enter.

"I'm not too late, am I?" she glanced at her watch as she spoke. "I had to make a quick stop at my office."

"No, it's okay, you're not late at all," he stammered.

That was not entirely true, but considering her appearance, he immediately forgave her. She wore a red sweater under a black leather coat that accentuates the intensity of her gray eyes. He appreciated her slim figure, trying with difficulty not to stare as his gaze shifted down to her black pants. She peeled out of her coat and slung it over her arm while looking at him nervously.

Maya was caught off guard by his intensely blue eyes and striking good looks. He was far more handsome than his profile picture and extremely tall. He hovered over her.

Maya handed Scott a bottle of Sauvignon Blanc. He took her coat and hung it in the closet before leading her towards the kitchen.

"Please, sit down."

She sat at the kitchen table and elegantly crossed her legs. Scott noticed her red toenails peeking through her black open-toe pumps and was again momentarily distracted.

"So, what do you think?" Maya asked

"You look great!"

"Excuse me?"

"I mean, it's excellent!" realizing she was referring to the wine. Scott was embarrassed by his unabashed admiration.

Maya smiled in turn. "Thanks, you look great too."

"That is a fantastic outfit."

Maya looked down at her hands resting on the table and then demurely back at Scott.

"I'm sorry, I've embarrassed you, haven't I?" he asked.

"Not really. I appreciate the compliment but the men I meet are usually not so forthright or complimenting."

"You're kidding?"

"No really..." she began but stopped halfway through her sentence.

"Go ahead Maya, so you were saying that most men you meet aren't wise enough to recognize your beauty and tell you so?"

"Yes, I guess that must be it," Maya smile warmly, feeling more comfortable now.

"So, are you hungry?" Scott asks, nearly melting at the glimmer of her gray eyes.

"What are you cooking."

"Come see." Maya took a few hesitant steps and look at the pots.

"Mmm. That looks delicious."

Then she looked at Scott. She smiled and suppressed her laughter.

"Scott?"

"Yes?" his blue eyes gleaming mischievously.

"What are you wearing?"

He had forgotten that he was wearing an apron tied around his neck, emblazoned with "Kiss the Cook" in large black letters across the chest. It was a gift from his sisters Ingrid and Petra.

"Not very subtle, is it?"

"No, it's not subtle, but I like it!" Maya said, laughing, leaned over, boldly planting a tiny kiss on his cheeks.

"Thanks," he laughed, turning back to the pot, stopping himself from kissing her back.

"Can I interest you in a glass of wine?" Scott was happy to find something else to do lest he grab her around the waist and smolder her with kisses right there in the kitchen.

"Sure."

Scott handed her a glass of wine.

"Prost."

"Prost?" she asked.

"Prost is Cheers in German."

Their glasses clinked, and as the wine touch their lips, their glances met. Scott gazed into Maya's beautiful grey eyes and began ticking off the minutes until dinner, knowing that every moment he wasn't touching her would be torture.

"Perfect," Maya said as she sipped the wine.

"Yes, you are," Scott replied, and Maya's expression lit up from the generous compliment.

"Thank you for coming, I love to cook, and this is my first opportunity to make dinner for you, I hope you like it and I hope it would be the first of many."

Scott set his glass down and added shrimp to the vegetables in the pan.

"You must be starving; I promise it will be worth it."

"I am sure it will be worth the wait."

"Tonight, you are going to experience a little heaven on earth," he said smiling.

"Oh," Maya asked.

Scott shot her a smoldering look. "And I'm not just talking about food."

Maya laughed the melodic laugh that Scott loved to hear. The glow from the candles illuminated her wavy dark brown long hair, and he watched her coyly tuck a strand behind her ear.

Leaving the shrimp and vegetables to simmer, he took a few steps towards Maya.

"I want to kiss you right now, but if I do, I don't think we'll make it to dinner."

Maya smiled, and Scott watched her eyes sparkle mischievously.

"I am certain we won't."

"You are driving me crazy, he whispered. "I want you so badly, but not like this. I want us to take our time, to make this last. I know you are 'The Real Thing.'"

They both smiled, locked in each other's eyes.

The first moment he touched her; he dominated her whole soul. Maya had never felt anything like it before. The memories of her teenage dreams came flooding back, he was everything she ever dreamed of. Maya felt out of control in her heart. She was scared and excited at the same time. She would fall asleep listening to Scott's magical voice on the phone in the wee hours of the morning. She had never done this before. She felt like a giddy teenager. When he was away from her, her body ached for his touch and tender kisses to return.

Scott was open-hearted and sensitive, and very sweet. He was kind and generous and when she finally broke down and told him her story, he instantly was loving and supportive. He fascinated her. He did not know how much he consumed her thoughts. She would get lost in him, everything was so beautiful, he was happy, and she could see it. He loves her family, especially her children.

Scott kept telling Maya there is no turning back, and that one day he will not let her go. She learned more about him than she did any other person in her life. Maya wanted to trust the love, to understand that she now has a more meaningful relationship with her children because of Scott's passion. He made her realise that because she was living her life, and she was happy and contended, that energy attracted him.

Maya had never been happier and realized she had never been in love like this. Scott was everything that she had dreamed a partner would be. And Maya thought because he had come into her life now, that she was ready, she had healed enough to date again. Maya had already been through more hardship than anyone can possibly imagine. She was still afraid, still skeptical, but she decided to open her heart once more.

And she was so glad she did.

"It was God working in mysterious ways. I would have stayed single," Maya told her sisters. "Love comes at unexpected times and in unexpected places."

This was the beginning of the most beautiful, loving relationship. Maya and Scott traveled worldwide, drove across the U.S, India, Nepal, Dubai, and Germany. They took dance lessons, attended the theater, concerts, and lectures together. He brought a level of love and fulfillment into Maya's life that she had stopped believing existed.

A few months later, Scott proposed to Maya on her birthday. She was pleasantly surprised to find her children already at the restaurant waiting for them and was so happy they could join them for dinner. Little did she know that Scott had already told them he was about to propose. It was beautiful, and she immediately said yes.

They got married on the beautiful sandy beaches of Cayo Coco, surrounded by all their friends and family.

"I don't know that I would have jumped into the dating pool any time soon. I was just taken aback by her, by her beauty, her kindness, her genuineness, and her love for life, despite what she has been through. She impressed me immensely," he said during his speech.

Maya did take a minute to step away from the wedding celebrations, and in a quiet moment down by the water, she reflected on her life and the crazy journey it took to get here. Scott's favourite song — Three Little Birds, by Bob Marley — was playing softly, the beautiful Cuban sunset in the background. She took a sip of her champagne and smiled. She always knew this day would come, and she would indeed find true love and happiness.

Maya was busy at work on the corporation's next year fiscal budget when her phone dinged.

Scott: "Hey 'The Real Thing.'"
The Real Thing: "Hey you."
Scott: "Am In a lucky guy or what?"
The Real Thing: "I'd say we're both pretty lucky."
Scott: "Maybe we should contact Match.com and do one of the cheesy television commercials?"

The Real Thing: "That is a great idea, but I have a better one. Let's take a trip back to our wedding destination spot."
Scott: "Absolutely."

As Maya and Scott sat on the beach sipping Rum and Coke, and listening to Scott's favourite Bob Marley tunes, Maya reflects at her life and the life of her sisters, her mother, and her grandmother.

Maya knew that she would have to tell their stories one day. One day very soon.

THE END

Glossary

PHRASE	MEANING
Belay the puri	Rolling the dough.
Bhariat	Groom's wedding procession.
Catahar	In the same family as Breadfruit.
Chicken curry	A typical curry from the Indian subcontinent consists of chicken stewed in an onion- and tomato-based sauce, flavoured with ginger, garlic, tomato puree, chilli peppers and a variety of spices, often including turmeric, cumin, coriander, cinnamon, and cardamom.
Cook night	In Guyana, this night the men and women cut up vegetables for the next day feast. The cook night has always provided the opportunity for dancing, fun and teasing of the bride and groom.

PHRASE	MEANING
Coolie people	A person of East Indian ancestry. Most Caribbean people of East Indian descent can trace their roots back to indentured workers imported by the British in the 19th century after the abolition of slavery.
Daru	Alcohol.
Dhal puri	Flat bread stuffed with seasoned yellow split peas.
Dig dutty	It is popular mainly in Guyana is essentially prayers to Mother Earth and is done two days prior to the wedding.
Dupatta	Dupatta is a long headscarf popular in traditional clothing of many South Indian cultures. Also called a chunni and can be draped over the head and shoulders in many different ways.
Dye rubbing	Turmeric powder or dye is mixed with oil and is anointed on to the bodies of bride and groom in two cycles, one in the morning and one in the evening. It is performed by a group of five or seven unmarried young girls.
Firesides	Fireside is an oven that is typically made with mud or clay and covered with a mixture of cow dung and mud. The Fireside is typically made on a wooden stand.
From away	A term used in Guyana for someone who lives in another country and came to visit.
Girlish	Characteristics of a girl.

PHRASE	MEANING
Goat curry	A typical curry from the Indian subcontinent consists of goat stewed in an onion- and tomato-based sauce, flavoured with ginger, garlic, tomato puree, chilli peppers and a variety of spices, often including turmeric, cumin, coriander, cinnamon, and cardamom.
Halwa & Puri	Halwa & Puri is a traditional Indian dish that features semolina pudding or halwa, then combined with sugars, nuts such as pistachios and almonds, and a soft fried dough called puri.
Hanuman chalisa	The Hanuman Chalisa is a Hindu devotional hymn in praise of Lord Hanuman. Composed of 40 verses filled with praises for Lord Hanuman It is said to bestow protection from illness, adversaries, and adversities.
Holi	Holi is a popular ancient Indian festival, also known as the Festival of Love, the Festival of Colours and the Festival of Spring. It also signifies the triumph of good over the evil. It is celebrated in India, Nepal the Caribbean, Canada and the United States of America.
Jhumkas	It is a kind of Indian style earrings that have the shape of an inverted bell.
Kheer	Rice pudding made with rice, sugar, milk and flavored with cardamom, nuts, and touch of rose water.

PHRASE	MEANING
Kingpin	A person that is essential to the head or the success of an organization or operation.
Kuch Gadbad Hai	Popular West Indian song.
Lotus Leaf	The lotus leaf has been used as a Guyanese tradition for many years. People often eat food in it, and they also eat with their hands.
Maaro	Nuptial Canopy.
Maticoor	Also known as dig dutty. It is popular mainly in Guyana and is essentially prayers to Mother Earth. It is done is done two days prior to the wedding.
Naam samskara	The formal naming Hindu ceremony performed to select a newborn's name using traditional methods and following the astrological rules of naming.
Nine days	The tradition has guests bring gifts, including gold bangle bracelets for both boy and girl babies; it is also customarily when moms take their first post-delivery bath.
Paki	Paki is a term typically directed towards people of Pakistani descent, and as a racial slur is often used indiscriminately towards people of perceived South Asian decent.

PHRASE	MEANING
Potato curry	A typical curry from the Indian subcontinent consists of potatoes, stewed in an onion- and tomato-based sauce, flavoured with ginger, garlic, tomato puree, chilli peppers and a variety of spices, often including turmeric, cumin, coriander, cinnamon, and cardamom.
Puja	Puja, the loving offering of light, flowers, and water or food to the divine, is the essential ritual of Hinduism.
Puri	A light, round, unleavened wheat bread & Ghee, usually deep-fried.
Seven curry	Seven curry is a traditional Indo-Guyanese delicacy prepared and served at Hindu religious functions. This consists of seven different types of vegetarian curry including pumpkin, bhagee (spinach), katahar, potato/channa (chick peas), balange (eggplant), edoe and dhal and is usually served in a water-lily leaf. Mango and achar are served on the side.
Tikka	Dot placed to ward off the evil eye.
Wedding House	Place or venue for the wedding.

About The Author

Sandy Maeck is a Toronto based Author. Born Shobha Maraj, to a prominent family in Georgetown, Guyana. Her father is from the distinguished Maraj family of Kitty, and her mother is from the well-known Persaud-Sharma family of Alexander Village.

She grew up in a strong Hindu home yet went to Catholic school most of her life. She attended the Indian Cultural Centre at the age of thirteen, to learn Classical Indian Dance.

Sandy migrated to Canada in 1985, due to an arranged marriage. Although she had a passion for writing and dancing, her life did not allow her that luxury. Amongst the struggles of being a single mother of four children and facing hardships in failed marriages, Sandy worked as a leader in one of the largest Toronto-based telecommunications companies for many years before accepting an offer to attend an employer paid University program in Geographical Information Systems. After continuing to work in the GIS department for some years, she accepted a payout to start a new venture.

Sandy was then employed with the Federal Government for a few years before venturing to Florida, where she found her passion for the Condominium Industry. Moving back to Canada and amidst her hardships, she managed to acquire her RCM and OLCM designations to become a successful Senior Condominium Property Manager as well as the founder of two successful businesses.

Sandy is the founder and Artistic Director of STCC Dance Academy and Owner and Director of Shobha's Wedding Services.

Sandy is a continually active volunteer in her community for the past twenty-five years and is currently a Director at Devi Mandir in Pickering. Part of her responsibility is planning the cultural programs as well as fundraising. She is the recipient of numerous volunteer awards, including the Civic Award from the Town of Pickering.

Sandy has four children and three grandchildren and now lives in Toronto with her loving husband and youngest son.

In her spare time, Sandy enjoys teaching Indian dance, volunteering, painting, and gardening.